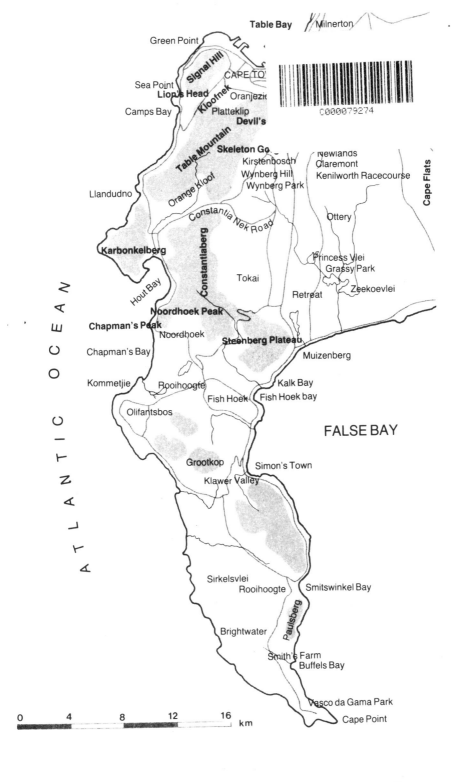

Table Bay / Milnerton

Green Point

Signal Hill

CAPE TO

Sea Point

Lion's Head   Oranjezi

Kloofnek

Camps Bay   Platteklip

Devil's

Table Mountain   Skeleton Go

Kirstenbosch   Newlands
Claremont
Wynberg Hill   Kenilworth Racecourse

Orange Kloof   Wynberg Park

Llandudno

Constantia Nek Road

Cape Flats

Ottery

Karbonkelberg   Constantiaberg

Princess Vlei
Grassy Park

Tokai   Zeekoevlei

Retreat

Hout Bay

Noordhoek Peak

Chapman's Peak   Steenberg Plateau

Noordhoek   Muizenberg

Chapman's Bay

Kommetjie   Rooihoogte   Kalk Bay

Fish Hoek   Fish Hoek bay

Olifantsbos

FALSE BAY

A T L A N T I C   O C E A N

Grootkop   Simon's Town

Klawer Valley

Sirkelsvlei   Smitswinkel Bay

Rooihoogte

Paulsberg

Brightwater

Smith's Farm
Buffels Bay

Vasco da Gama Park

Cape Point

0   4   8   12   16
km

Cape Peninsula

Cape Peninsula

South African Wild Flower Guide 3

Drawings and text by
Mary Maytham Kidd

including the original foreword
by the Rt. Hon. Field-Marshal J.C. Smuts

Revision of botanical names
by Terry Trinder-Smith

This guide is the third
in a series of Wild Flower Guides
published by the Botanical Society
of South Africa

The Botanical Society of South Africa was founded in 1913 to support the National Botanic Gardens, to promote the conservation and cultivation of our indigenous flora and to provide environmental education.

One of our projects is the publication of a series of wild flower guides.

Published to date are:

Guide 1: Namaqualand and Clanwilliam	1981 (out of print)
Guide 1: (revised): Namaqualand	1988
Guide 2: Outeniqua, Tsitsikamma & Eastern Little Karoo	1982
Guide 3: Cape Peninsula	1983
Guide 4: Transvaal Lowveld & Escarpment	1984
Guide 5: Hottentots Holland to Hermanus	1985
Guide 6: Karoo	1994

Opposite title page: *Disa uniflora*, the Pride of Table Mountain. (Percy Sargeant)

First published 1950 Oxford University Press
2nd edition 1973 Oxford University Press

3rd edition 1983
4th edition 1996
Botanical Society of South Africa
Kirstenbosch, Claremont, 7735, RSA

Typesetting by Wouter Reinders
Reproduction by Hirt & Carter
Printed and bound by CTP Book Printers, Caxton Street, Parow

ISBN 0 620 6746 2

Preface to the 4th edition (1996)

In this 4th edition of our *Wild Flower Guide 3: Cape Peninsula*, the text and nomenclature have been corrected and revised by Mr Terry Trinder-Smith of the Bolus Herbarium, University of Cape Town, following his recent, exhaustive studies on the flora of the Cape Peninsula. The Publications Committee of the Botanical Society of South Africa is most appreciative of his expert assistance in updating the text.

Originally published in 1950 by Oxford University Press as *Wild Flowers of the Cape Peninsula*, over 23 000 copies have been sold during the 45 years it has remained in print. Demand for this classic work remains steady both from residents and ever increasing numbers of interested visitors. It is hoped therefore that this new edition will continue to serve as a useful identification guide to the more prominent plants indigenous to the Cape Peninsula.

At the time of going to press, steps were being taken towards the proclamation of a National Park on the Cape Peninsula extending from Table Mountain to Cape Point. The Botanical Society of South Africa applauds this move towards the more effective conservation of this area's flora.

J. P. ROURKE
Chairman, Publications Committee
Botanical Society of South Africa

Contents

Hypodiscus aristatus, typifying the restio component of the Fynbos
(A.V. Hall)

These guides are made possible through the co-operation of members of the public and private sector through their dedication to the conservation of our floral wealth. The Publications Committee that has motivated the series consists of representatives from the following bodies: the Botanical Society of South Africa, Cape Nature Conservation, the National Botanical Institute, the University of Cape Town's Bolus Herbarium.

Acknowledgements

Many years ago I enjoyed compiling a book to guide beginners towards naming the many wild flowers of the Cape Peninsula for themselves. As mentioned in the historical note so kindly compiled for the 1983 edition by Dr John Rourke of the Compton Herbarium, I was privileged to have the help and support of the leading botanists of that era.

Although a second edition was produced in 1973, it had been out of print for a number of years. Then, following frequent requests for a guide to the Cape flora, Lt Cdr R. Geary-Cooke and Mrs Kay Bergh of the Botanical Society asked me to allow them to include my book in the Society's present series of wild flower guides.

As the intentions of the Society in publishing this series was identical to mine in the 1940s, I am delighted to contribute to this project.

Foremost I am indebted to Mrs Pauline Fairall of the Compton Herbarium who for many years has been recording the changes to the botanical names used in my book. She has supervised a complete revision of the nomenclature. Miss Christien Malan and Miss Lovell Bosman of the National Botanical Gardens have assisted with the common names and correcting the text.

Prof. E.A. Schelpe, Director of the Bolus Herbarium of the University of Cape Town, Associate Professor Anthony Hall and Mrs Elizabeth Ashton, also of the University, provided material for the interesting and informative new introduction.

My special thanks go to Miss Annelise le Roux and Mr and Mrs W.J. le Roux who have translated this new edition, thereby producing the first Afrikaans edition.

Mr E.G.H. Oliver of the Botanical Research Institute kindly checked the entire guide and provided many helpful comments. Mr Percy Sargeant, Miss Zelda Wahl of the Department of Nature and Environmental Conservation and Associate Professor Anthony Hall provided the photographs, illustrating the introduction so well. I am indebted to Mrs Fay Geary-Cooke for her help in judging the reproduction of the drawings.

I am most indebted to Mr Wim Reinders for the time and effort he has put into the design of this new edition and to Mrs Pat Coley and Mrs Kay Bergh, who, in their role as joint editors have, with patience and understanding, brought this guide to completion.

MARY MAYTHAM KIDD
1983

Historical note

During October 1950, the first edition of Mary Maytham Kidd's *Wild Flowers of the Cape Peninsula* appeared in bookshops throughout South Africa. As a compact field handbook, illustrating some 814 species of flowering plants indigenous to the Cape Peninsula, it stood alone – nothing like it had ever appeared in this country before. That first edition of 7 000 copies was followed by a second edition in 1973, a third edition, of 11 000 English copies and 4 000 Afrikaans copies, which was included in the Botanical Society's S.A. Wild Flower Guide Series in 1983 and now by this fourth edition.

It all began shortly before the outbreak of the second world war. In November 1938, soon after returning to South Africa from England as a young woman of twenty-four, Mary Maytham journeyed to Simonstown to visit her old Roedean headmistresses, Miss T.E. Lawrence, Miss K.M. Earle and vice-principal, Miss R. Scott, who were living there in retirement. As all were keenly interested in wild flowers a drive to Cape Point followed. In those days identifying the specimens encountered was a major problem as there were no popular illustrated publications to consult. Knowing of Mary Maytham's artistic ability (she had won a school prize for drawing flowers), it is hardly surprising that this excursion with her former schoolmistresses should have occasioned a bold suggestion: "Why don't you illustrate a book on wild flowers?". The idea appealed to Mary Maytham and a few weeks later, in January 1939, the first illustrations had been completed.

It was soon obvious that expert guidance from a botanist was needed and so, not unnaturally, advice was sought from the then doyenne of Cape botanists, Dr Louisa Bolus. Support was at once forthcoming with Dr. Bolus and her staff at the Bolus Herbarium – Neville Pillans, Elsie Esterhuysen and Frances Leighton (Mrs Isaacs) – assisting with the identifications.

Taxonomic accuracy was ensured from the outset. Specimens used for the preparation of the paintings were identified by the Bolus Herbarium's staff, as and when the illustrations were completed.

By 1943 the colour plates were ready for publication but no accompanying text had yet been prepared. World War II, its aftermath, a move to

Erica fairii, naturally confind to a single hectare in the Cape Peninsula. Some 31 other species illustrated in this guide are seldom seen or possibly extinct. (A.V. Hall)

England and Mary Maytham's marriage to Mr Hubert Kidd, interrupted any further progress until 1948. In retrospect, however, this five year delay was fortunate, as the definitive *Flora of the Cape Peninsula*, by Prof. R.S. Adamson and Capt. T.M. Salter, was also nearing completion. It was at this point that Capt. Salter stepped into the picture. Unpublished typescript contributions to the *Flora of the Cape Peninsula* were offered as source material for the text, thereby ensuring taxonomic and nomenclatural uniformity between the two works. Thus, with Salter's editorial guidance and support, the text was soon assembled.

Priced at three guineas in bookshops, *Wild Flowers of the Cape Peninsula* was considered a very expensive handbook in 1950, yet so great was the demand for it that half the edition was sold out within a year of publication.

Foreword *to the 1950 edition*

by the Rt. Hon. Field-Marsh. J.C. Smuts

It is a pleasure writing a foreword to introduce this book, with its beautiful paintings of the plants of the Cape Peninsula. When the authoress began these paintings I saw a number of them and told her I would be happy to sponsor her book when published. In her charming preface she disclaims any expert knowledge of botany and tells how she came to paint the Cape flowers. But in spite of her modesty I feel she has made a valuable contribution to our knowledge and enjoyment of the plant life of the Cape and that all lovers of our magnificent flora will be deeply indebted to her. The work has, in any case, been carefully vetted by expert botanical authority and is certain to be a valuable and permanent addition to our literature on the subject. To schools, especially, it should be an invaluable aid in the teaching of botany.

The public generally, even the botanical public, are far from fully aware of the beauty and wealth of our wonderful Cape flora. The Cape Peninsula is merely its western limit and, in fact, it extends along the coastal mountain ranges as far east as Port Elizabeth. It is distinct from the flora of the rest of the African continent, even of the rest of South Africa. Many of our beautiful flowers are, of course, well known far beyond South Africa and may be seen in public and private collections in other parts of the world. But people are not aware that originally they came from the Cape, where they were collected in the eighteenth and early nineteenth centuries by European botanists and collectors, sent to the Cape expressly for the purpose, and domesticated abroad. Many of the glories among flowers in gardens abroad are thus of South African origin, though this is not generally known and only botanists are aware of the real facts.

Our Cape plants belong to a flora which is unique and to which a great deal of mystery attaches. A large number of plant families belonging to our flora are found nowhere else in the world and have only distant relatives in a few Southern countries like West Australia and South America. And the question of the origin of this unique flora has intrigued students of the geographical distribution of plants. Great authorities, like Sir Joseph Hooker, who made a special study of the question, and Charles Darwin, inclined to the view that they derive from a lost continent now under the Indian or Southern ocean, of which Antarctica is now the main survival, and that the Northern limits of the lost continent may have reached as far north as the tip of South Africa and may thus have passed on its unique southern flora

Kirstenbosch Botanical Garden in spring. Field-Marshal Smuts' favourite ascent up Table Mountain leads through the indigenous forest of Skeleton Gorge, which can be seen in the background. (A.V. Hall)

as far north. It is noteworthy that the Cape flora is confined to this southern tip of Africa, as I have already stated, and that the rest, even of South Africa, is covered by a northern flora which has reached so far south.

Such at least is speculation, and for the rest the frozen Antarctic holds its secrets, which may, however, eventually be revealed by the discovery of plant fossils under its ancient ice cover. Only then, if at all, will this mystery be solved.

True it is that when the European botanists came to the Cape in the seventeenth and eighteenth centuries they found here an unrecognizable plant life, quite unlike that of Europe. New names had to be invented for whole families, not to mention numerous genera and species. Everything looked new and strange. A new botanical world had been discovered, of unique and strange characters. Such is our Cape flora. Some exotics have indeed since come from overseas. Still more plants are intruders, which have come by land from the North, in the ways common in plant migration. But the bulk of this flora was indigenous and new to science. We can imagine the surprise of these early European botanists at this strange sight, this faery land of flowers from nowhere. They must have been, like stout Cortes and his gallant band when they stared upon the vast Pacific, "silent upon a peak in Darien". Northern botanists, determined to prove a Northern origin for our botany, have done their best to assimiliate our flora to that of the north. But in vain: the strange, fascinating lady keeps her secret and her charm. The mystery probably points to some ancient tragedy in the life history of this great globe itself. Who knows?

This is the Cape flora, of which much is portrayed in this book, unique, mysterious, but lovely and a joy for ever. This is a happy land, where one can live in company of such flowers, enjoy them, answer their appeal and be absorbed and fascinated by them. Surely there is nothing more wonderful in the wide world than this Peninsula, set among the seas, girdled by the mountains, with its clear benign air by day, its starlit heavens by night and its heritage from the distant past of our incomparable floral wealth. Nature has contributed enough, sometimes even more than one can bear. If anything more is wanted it must be contributed by Art.

And so we can also contemplate this beauty, this floral wealth, through the medium of our human art, see it in beautiful reproductions, such as this book puts before us. We can take it with us when through change of season, or in absence from home, we cannot carry the beloved presence with us. Through Art the beloved scene remains with us.

This book thus supplements and adds to the opportunities of enjoying the loveliness that is in our flowers and the message that they have for the human spirit. Lovers of our flora will thus be deeply indebted to our authoress for her service, a true service of love, in the preparation of a book which must have involved much labour and occupied much time.

(Overleaf) The Cape of Good Hope, separating the cold Atlantic from the warmer water of False Bay. A typical summer south-east cloud obscures Table Mountain in the distance, (Zelda Wahl, Cape Nature Conservation)

Introduction

The Cape Floristic Kingdom is one of the unique floras of the world. It extends from Vanrhynsdorp southwards to the Cape Peninsula (250 km) and east to near Grahamstown (800 km) in a broken belt 40-150 km wide. It is the richest flora in the world, with 1 300 species per 10 000 km² as against 385 and 420 for its nearest known competitors in South America and a probable 580 for New Guinea. Most of its species are very distinctive and confined to this comparatively small area. Its uniqueness and diversity have earned it special recognition as one of the six main floristic kingdoms. It ranks with the Boreal Floristic Kingdom which covers the northern hemisphere north of the great deserts, an area thouands of times larger than the natural home of the Fynbos.

The Cape Peninsula alone is the home of over 2 600 species of flowering plants in an area of only about 500 km². This is more than the total number of species found in South Australia or the British Isles.

This guide is a new edition of *Wildflowers of the Cape Peninsula* by Mary Maytham Kidd. The 814 drawings of flowers have been reproduced from the original artwork, which was completed in 1943. Since that time a number of these plants have virtually disappeared; and there is scientific evidence of this in the case of 31 of the species illustrated. These are marked with●. The Cape Peninsula has today over 150 rare and threatened plants.

Geology and soils
The Cape Peninsula has all the scenic qualities of a great national park, with a magnificent 50 km chain of steep rugged mountains, broken by small coastal valleys that form miniature landscapes ringed by bold cliffs on the skyline. Dominated by Table Mountain and the outlying Lion's Head and Devil's Peak, the mountains extend southwards towards Cape Point. To the north-east, the low-lying Cape Flats join the Peninsula to the mountainous mainland.

The mountains are composed of a pale coloured quartzitic sandstone (Table Mountain Sandstone) which has been greyed by the growth of lichens. This sandstone was levelled by ice some 300 million years ago, long before the inland sandstone mountains were so spectacularly folded and crumpled. Below the sandstone, the Malmesbury Shale gives the smooth,

Lion's Head with Table Mountain in the background, showing the layers of Table Mountain Sandstone and a granite intrusion below Lion's Head.
(Zelda Wahl, Cape Nature Conservation)

rounded contour to the Lion's Rump and underlies central Cape Town. The granite that was intruded is obvious along many rocky shorelines as massive grey boulders. The sandstone has broken down into mineral-deficient sands which are very well drained except where peaty marshes have developed in rock basins. These soils are dry in summer, have poor water retention and very low concentrations of important nutrients such as potassium and phosphorus, but nevertheless support this extraordinary flora. The Malmesbury Shales produce a fine-grained fertile soil and the granite has weathered to form clays of varying grittiness and fertility.

Recent sands cover parts of some of the valleys, such as at Fish Hoek and the Cape Flats. Research indicates these are partly of marine origin, blown in from ancient shorelines which shifted back and forth during the world glacial and interglacial periods with successive uptakes and releases of water from vast ice sheets in colder climate regions. It is interesting to reflect that for much of the past 1,6 million years False Bay was empty and the west coast 15 km from its present line.

Climate

The Cape Peninsula enjoys a Mediterranean climate, with warm, dry summers and cold, wet winters; however, frosts are light and snow rarely falls on Table Mountain. Rainfall varies considerably in different parts of the Peninsula. The mean annual rainfall at the highest point of Table Mountain (1 083 m) is approximately 1 900 mm; at Kirstenbosch it is about 1 340 mm and on Signal Hill and at Cape Point it drops to 457 mm and 305 mm respectively. On the mountains, however, the summer drought is alleviated by the mists associated with the south easterly winds, such as the 'tablecloth' which often envelops the summit plateaux of Table Mountain and also the lower mountains to the south. Many plant species, for example *Disa uniflora* (p. 40), are confined on Table Mountain to the summer mist belt.

Slopes differ in local climate according to the amount of exposure to the sun. North-facing slopes are generally hotter and drier than those facing south in the southern hemisphere. The local climate of a deeply-sheltered kloof will be moister and cooler than an exposed aspect. These factors provide the wide range of ecological niches which are occupied by the amazing variety of plant communitites one sees on any walk in the Peninsula mountains.

Clues to the events of the past on the Cape Peninsula come from geologists' cores taken from a 60 m deep peat deposit a kilometre south of Chapman's Peak. The cores bear fossil pollens giving a continuous record of the plants of the Noordhoek basin for the past 25 million years, a quarter of the age of the flowering plants. Studies of the cores indicate first an

Fynbos above Kommetjie, showing species of *Erica*, *Leucaendron*, various Asteraceae and Restionaceae. (Percy Sargeant)

ancient vegetation with palms, then the gradual appearance of the heath-flora of the Cape. It appears that about five million years ago the vegetation rapidly diversified into the species-rich flora we see today.

Plant life

Two main vegetation types are represented on the Cape Peninsula, hard-leafed scrub or bush, commonly known as Fynbos, and evergreen forest confined to sheltered ravines.

Fynbos

The predominant vegetation is Fynbos, the famous heath, reed and protea flora found in the coastal plains and mountains of the south-western and southern Cape Province. There are two possible origins of the name Fynbos (fine bush): this refers either to the small leaves of many of the bushes or the rich variety of the plants. It can be recognized by the usual presence of three kinds of plant: the heath-like Ericas; the Cape Reed or Restio family; and members of the Protea family.

Fynbos consists mainly of knee-high vegetation, with the Restio family predominating, interspersed with taller members of the Protea family grow-

Watsonia zeyheri flowering after a fire on the road to Olifantsbos in the Cape of Good Hope Nature Reserve. Note that the drier slopes of the hillside show no sign of post-fire recovery. (Percy Sargeant)

ing as isolated bushes or as continuous groves. Marshes and streamsides have a denser and taller growth, while on dry, exposed slopes, the plants are lower and spaced apart. Of the few tree species associated with the Fynbos, two of the most obvious are the Silvertree (*Leucadendron argenteum*) and the Wild Almond (*Brabejum stellatifolium*) (p. 42). The latter was planted to form a boundary hedge by Van Riebeeck and portions of this may still be seen in Kirstenbosch.

Many other kinds of plants are common elements in Fynbos, as users of this guide will discover: often abundant are the Daisy family (*Asteraceae*) and many plants from the Pea family (*Fabaceae*). Some of the more spectacular plants are those with bulbs, corms and rhizomes which are members of the Iris and Lily families (*Iridaceae* and *Liliaceae*): these provide spectacular displays of flowers in early summer, especially after fires. The Peninsula has over 100 kinds of ground orchid, many of them rare and difficult to find, but representing almost a quarter of all the orchids of southern Africa. There are also some astonishing parasites with unusual flower-structures; very beautiful insectivorous plants; succulents with close relatives in the Karoo; wonderfully scented, small-fruited members of the Citrus family and much else to lure the plant explorer and photographer. Rarity lends

Coatal vegetation at Cape Maclear in spring, showing Mesembryanthemaceae and Asteraceae. (Percy Sargeant)

much interest to the flora: just under 100 plants are naturally restricted to the Cape Peninsula and many are confined to a few precious hectares of habitat.

Along the coasts of the south-western Cape a broad-leaved, shrubby vegetation occurs that is well adapted to the rigours of life in a windy, sometimes spray-soaked habitat on dry, sandy soils near the sea. Shallow lakes or vleis represent special habitats which have been extensively altered or destroyed in the forty five years between this edition and the first in 1950. Fynbos plants dominate the shores of some, such as those in the Cape of Good Hope Nature Reserve. Others, such as Sandvlei and Rondevlei, have extensive beds of bullrushes (*Typha*) and reeds (*Phragmites*), plants which occur widely elsewhere. Another habitat is the salt-marsh, now lost on the Cape Peninsula to industry at Paarden Eiland and to marina development at Noordhoek. This, with its peculiar succulent flora, survives to the north at Rietvlei near Milnerton, where it is a major habitat of migrant waders, some of which, amazingly, fly each year all the way from the Arctic.

Forest
The indigenous forest trees on the Peninsula include Yellowwood

(*Podocarpus latifolius*) (p. 42), Stinkwood (*Ocotea bullata*) (p. 42), Assegai (*Curtisia dentata*) (p. 42) and the Ironwood (*Olea capensis*) (p. 60). Many of these valuable timber trees were felled by the early settlers and the indigenous forests have been much reduced since Van Riebeeck's landing at the Cape.

Associated with the forest is a marginal community of broad-leaved shrubs, which is particularly apparent in less sheltered areas. The community can be recognized by its dark green, hard leaves that are much larger than the usual in Fynbos, with bushes such as Lepelhout (*Cassine*) (p. 72), Kershout (*Pterocelastrus*) (p. 72) and a few other plants that may grow into substantial trees, such as Wild Olive (*Olea*) (p. 64), White Milkwood (p. 60) and *Tarchonanthus* (p. 60). The white Milkwood has extremely close growth-rings and trunks a metre in diameter may be well over a thousand years old. The forests are very distinct from Fynbos. What is the origin of these forest patches? Are they remnants from an ancient, continuous forest-belt all along the Cape coast? They have many species in common with the famous Knysna forest. Found buried under gravel and the clays of the Cape Flats are some amazingly preserved tree trunks. Near a brickfield at Koelenhof, near Stellenbosch, dam-excavators found, in 1974, huge Yellowwood logs up to 26 metres long with some stumps still standing. Sealed under 12-14 metres of airtight clay, the wood has remained virtually undamaged for many thousands of years; in fact it could not be dated because it was beyond the 50 000 year range of the Carbon-14 method. Strangely, the wood could be identified as that of an Outeniqua Yellowwood, which today is found in nature no nearer than Swellendam. Fossil pollens from cores in the deep-cut, buried estuary at Rietvlei near Milnerton, also showed evidence of forest plants, as have repeated finds of buried wood in a belt from Crawford and Grassy Park to Pinelands and Bellville.

The future
Human population growth, presently undergoing astronomical growth, in South Africa and globally, carries in a large number of regions the threat of over-use of what the Earth can provide. The country that can conserve its resources will have a much better chance of surviving in the crowded future. Genetic diversity is one such resource: the immense range of plants and animals holds options for the future that may prove valuable for humanity in many ways. Local plants may have uses that today are still unknown, as sources of new medicines, breeding stock for crop and garden plants, as

Indigenous forest in the deep ravines at Noordhoek. The fynbos is separated from forest by a marginal community of broad-leaved shrubs. (Percy Sargeant)

Fynbos in a marsh on Red Hill. A striking clump of *Elegia cuspidata* is noticeable in the centre. (Percy Sargeant)

sources of plant cover for steep, erodable slopes and perhaps as future material for genetic manipulation for a variety of purposes ranging from foods to fibres.

At present the flora of the Cape Peninsula is mainly appreciated for its aesthetic values by the large urban population and tourist industry: it is a privilege simply to be able to walk through this great wonder of Nature, the world's most concentrated flora.

We must also remember there is an ethical responsibility not to spoil the Earth by destroying species that might be enjoyed or needed by future generations. As the dominant species on the planet, humanity should act upon a moral responsibility not to threaten unduly the other organisms sharing the Earth with us.

Threats and losses

Recent studies indicate that the Cape Peninsula has some 167 plant species in hazard: 30 of these are endangered and on the brink of extinction and 68 are critically rare. Added to this is the sombre fact that seven plants have become extinct on the Cape Peninsula by human action. This is understandable in view of the exceptional numbers of plants with very small geographical ranges. For example, one can name half a dozen heaths on the Peninsula alone with ranges covering less than a couple of hectares.

The worst pressure on the indigenous flora comes from the invasive plants imported from other countries for uses such as fixing sand-dunes, hedges, timber, firewood and stock-fodder,and now escaped to smother huge areas of natural plant-life with vast monotonous thickets. The black-list of these plants is lengthy: Rooikrans, Port Jackson, Long-leaved Acacia, Black Wattle, Blackwood, Sesbania, Silky Hakea, Rock Hakea, Cluster Pine, Australian Myrtle and Bramble.* A single Australian Port Jackson tree can shed 10 000 seeds per square metre a year and each seed is capable of surviving in the soil and germinating over a very long period of time. The alien invaders are usually greatly helped by fire. Their great seed output is mostly unimpaired by local seed-eating insects and birds and seeds are often adapted to germinate after a veld-fire. They grow quickly and soon over-top the Fynbos plants with dense and smothering growth. In a sample study of 200 recently extinct and severely threatened plants, the future of 54% had been jeopardised by alien plants.

Over 300 introduced plants have become established in the Peninsula. The more attractive of these are illustrated in this guide and are marked with a ♦.

An effect of over-frequent veld-fires is to suppress the Fynbos plants that require a number of years to restore stocks of seed in the soil to survive the next fire. This is especially serious for some of the large and beautiful Proteaceae such as *Aulax* which had a fine colony, the only one on the Peninsula, wiped out by fire. Combined with the stimulus it gives to aliens, fire may be truly disastrous and it has as yet unknown effects on vital animal associates such as pollinators and seed dispersers. Many Fynbos plants, especially the bulbs, have some adaptations to fire and may indeed require it occasionally, but regular burning may be responsible for some of the tragic extinctions.

Much of the original vegetation of the Cape Peninsula has already disappeared due to urban expansion, the spread of invasive exotic plants, too frequent fires and flower picking. Fortunately much still remains in the Cape of Good Hope Nature Reserve and the Table Mountain Reserve and other areas on the mountain chain to the south. However, with population pressure increasing, more stringent conservation of the remaining indigenous vegetation and a wider education of the public has become necessary if this flora is to be enjoyed by posterity.

*See Stirton, C.H., ed. (1978): *Plant Invaders: beautiful but dangerous*. Cape Nature Conservation, Cape Town. pp. 175, illustrated.

How to use this guide

Over 800 species are illustrated in this guide, some twice to show variation in colour or form. The illustrations are mostly arranged in the sequence of months in which the plants are most likely to be found in flower; where they are grouped together according to habitat this is indicated by the headings.

The colour illustrations for this guide were completed by 1943. Today many of these plants have become rare, threatened or possibly extinct. These have been marked with a ●. The exotic species included are marked with a ◆.

Some of the local English and Afrikaans common names have been given. It must be pointed out that different names are given to the same species in different regions and not all of the regional names are given in this wild flower guide.

Separate indexes are provided for both scientific and common names. A list of families and genera shows the number of species occurring on the Cape Peninsula in each genus.

Further information
Contact the following organisations:

The Botanical Society of
  South Africa
Kirstenbosch
Claremont
7735
Tel: (021) 797 2090;
Fax: (021) 797 2376

The National Botanical Institute
  of South Africa
Private Bag X7
Kirstenbosch
Claremont
7735
Tel: (021) 762 1166;
Fax: (021) 762 3229

Cape Nature Conservation
Private Bag 9086
Cape Town
8000
Tel: 483 4051; Fax: (021) 230939

Plant descriptions

Mountains and Mountain Slopes

1. **Peucedanum ferulaceum.** APIACEAE (= UMBELLIFERAE). 500-900 mm; occasional on mountain slopes; Jan.-March.

2. **Selago corymbosa.** SELAGINACEAE. Erect; 300-900 mm; Dec-May.

3. **Aspalathus arida.** FABACEAE (= LEGUMINOSAE). Low or prostrate shrublet; occasional, Kenilworth Race Course; Sept.-Feb.; branches spine-tipped.

4. **Sebaea ambigua.** GENTIANACEAE. Annual; up to 300 mm; frequent, damp places on flats; Oct.-Jan.

5. **Prismatocarpus sessilis.** CAMPANULACEAE. Prostrate or straggling annual; frequent on sandy peat; Jan.-Mar.; flowers white fading to yellow or pale blue.

● 6. **Erica margaritacea.** ERICACEAE. 300-500 mm; occasional on flats, Kenilworth Race Course; Oct.-Mar.

7. **Berzelia abrotanoides.** BRUNIACEAE. *Fonteinbos, Kol-kol.* Shrub; 900 mm-1,5 m; local, plentiful in marshes, by streamsides in the south; Aug.-Jan.

8. **Syndesmanthus articulatus.** ERICACEAE. Up to 300 mm; common, flats; Jan.-Apr. The flowers differ from those of *Erica* in having only one seed.

9. **Wahlenbergia procumbens.** CAMPANULACEAE. Prostrate herb; often perennial; frequent, lawns and damp places; Oct.-Apr.

10. **Cuscuta nitida.** CONVOLVULACEAE. *Dodder.* A climbing parasite; occasional on flats and hill slopes; Dec.-Jan.; very sweet-scented.

Scale: life size

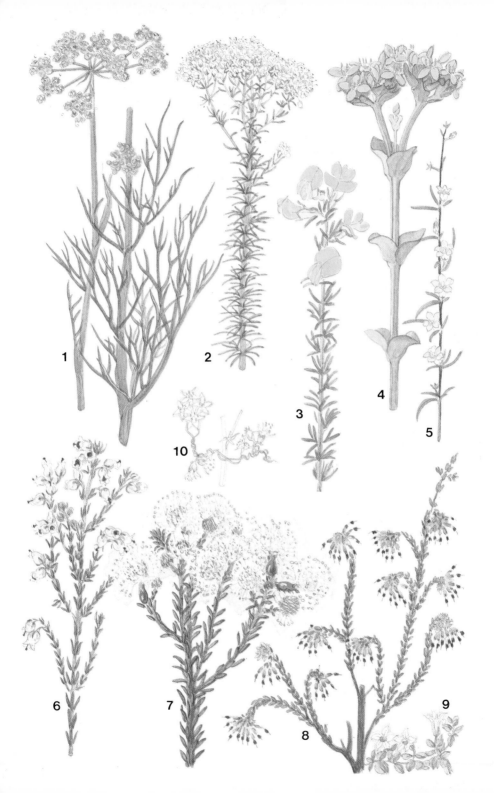

1. **Cotyledon orbiculata.** CRASSULACEAE. *Honde-oor, Varkoor, Kouterie, Plakkie.* Shrubby, rather succulent; up to 900 mm; frequent, especially near sea; Dec.-Jan.; poisonous.

2. **Harveya capensis.** SCROPHULARIACEAE. *White Harveya, Inkbos, Inkblom.* 100-500 mm; parasitic herb; occasional; Nov.-Feb.; like all harveyas it turns black when dried or pressed.

3. **Tylecodon grandiflorus.** (=Cotyledon grandiflora). CRASSULACEAE. Rather succulent; up to 900mm; occasional on dry western slopes; Jan.-Feb.

4. **Leonotis leonurus.** LAMIACEAE (=LABIATAE). *Wild Dagga, Minaret Flower.* Shrub; usually 1-2 m high; frequent; Nov.-Jan.

◆ 5. **Foeniculum vulgare.** APIACEAE (=UMBELLIFERAE). *Fennel, Vinkel.* 900 mm-3 m; common about suburbs; Dec.-Apr.; aromatic; native of Europe.

6. **Dilatris viscosa.** HAEMODORACEAE. *Bloedwortel.* 500-600 mm; occasional in swampy places above 620 m upwards; Aug.-Jan.

Scale: one-third life size

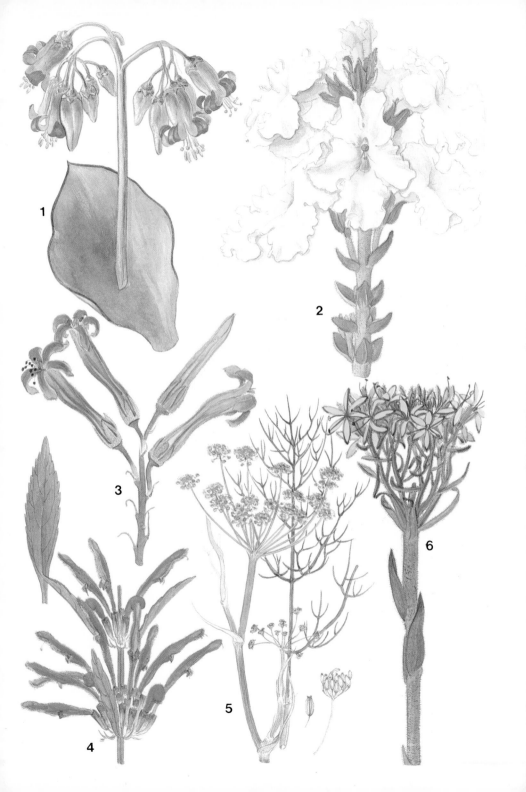

1

2

3

4

5

6

1. **Hermas villosa.** APIACEAE (=UMBELLIFERAE). Up to 900 mm; frequent on mountain slopes; Dec.-Mar.

2. **Agapanthus africanus.** ALLIACEAE (= LILIACEAE). 300-500 mm; common on upper slopes of mountains; Dec.-Jan.; especially after fires.

3. **Protea grandiceps.** PROTEACEAE. Shrub; 900 mm-1,5 m; rather rare at high altitudes – Devil's Peak, Platteklip, Kloof Corner, Spring Buttress; Jan.-Apr.

4. **Tritoniopsis triticea** (= Anapalina triticea). IRIDACEAE. Up to 500 mm; frequent in dry stony ground on upper mountain slopes and plateaux; Jan.-Feb.

Scale: one-third life size

1

2

3

4

1. **Caesia contorta.** ASPHODELACEAE (= LILIACEAE). Straggling; up to 300 mm; frequent; Nov.-Jan.; leaves in grass-like tufts.

2. **Psoralea asarina.** FABACEAE (= LEGUMINOSAE). Sprawling; common in northern areas; Oct.-Apr.

3. **Erica capensis** x **E. laeta** var. **incisa.** ERICACEAE. Natural hybrid; found in southern Peninsula.

4. **Erica laeta** var. **incisa.** ERICACEAE. 300-500 mm; common in marshy ground especially in the south; Dec.-Feb.

5. **Lampranthus falciformis.** MESEMBRYANTHEMACEAE. 70-300 mm; frequent on ledges and rocks on mountains; Nov.-Feb.

6. **Selago serrata.** SELAGINACEAE. More or less erect; 500-600 mm; frequent on mountain slopes among rocks; Oct.-Feb.

7. **Pelargonium pinnatum.** GERANIACEAE. Tuberous; 100-300 mm; frequent on hill slopes; Nov.-Jan; a variable species.

8. **Erica planifolia.** ERICACEAE. Dwarf, straggling; 150-300 mm; occasional on mountains in the south; July-Feb.

9. **Sutera hispida.** SCROPHULARIACEAE. Small shrublet; about 300 mm; common among bushes on hill slopes; Jan.-Dec.

10. **Itasina filifolia** (= Thunbergiella filiformis.). APIACEAE (= UMBELLIFERAE). 150-300 mm; common on sandy heathland, chiefly after fires; Nov.-Apr.

Scale: life size

1

2

3

4

5

6

7

8

9

10

1. **Phaenocoma prolifera.** ASTERACEAE (= COMPOSITAE). *Everlasting, Sewejaartjie.* Robust, shrublet; up to 610 mm; occasional from Muizenberg to the south; Nov.-Feb.

2. **Aspalathus barbata.** (= Borbonia barbata). FABACEAE (= LEGUMINOSAE). Robust, prickly shrublet; 300-600 mm, occasional on mountains above 465 m; Oct.-Jan.

● 3. **Herschelianthe forficaria** (= Herschelia forficaria). ORCHIDACEAE. Up to 300 mm; rare, Klaasjagersberg, once recorded in Klaver Valley; Jan.-Feb.

4. **Amphithalea imbricata.** FABACEAE (= LEGUMINOSAE). Shrub; up to 1,5 m; occasional in kloofs on the higher mountains; Dec.-June.

5. **Phylica dioica.** RHAMNACEAE. Rigid shrub; up to 900 mm; occasional in rocky places on upper mountain slopes; Dec.-Mar.

6. **Crassula coccinea** (= Rochea coccinea). CRASSULACEAE. *Red Crassula, Klipblom.* Up to 500 mm; frequent on mountain; Jan.-Mar.

7. **Erepsia anceps** (= E. gracilis). MESEMBRYANTHEMACEAE. Up to 300 mm; frequent on hillsides in northern areas; Jan.-Apr.

Scale: life size

1

2

3

4

5

6

7

Orchidaceae

1. **Disa uniflora.** *Red Disa, Pride of Table Mountain.* 300-500 mm; frequent by margins of mountain streams and in wet rocky clefts; Jan.-Mar.

2. **Disa uncinata.** 100-300 mm; occasional, damp shaded grassy places – Table Mountain and near Hout Bay; Oct.-Jan.

3. **Disa longicornis.** *Mauve Disa, Drip Disa.* 100-200 mm; local on wet, shaded rocky cliffs on Table Mountain and Constantiaberg; Dec.-Jan.

Scale: life size

Forest Trees

1. Podocarpus latifolius. PODOCARPACEAE. *Yellowwood, Geelhout.* Large tree, with purplish bark; occasional in mountain forests – Table Mountain to Simonstown; Oct.-Dec.; fruit January; male and female flowers borne on different trees, female illustrated.

2. Ilex mitis. AQUIFOLIACEAE. *Cape Holly, Waterhout, Without.* Large tree up to 15 m with smooth white bark; local, by streams – Kirstenbosch and Orange Kloof; Mar.; fruit Apr.

3. Ocotea bullata. LAURACEAE. *Stinkwood, Stinkhout.* Tree up to 9 m; rare in damp mountain forests – Kirstenbosch, Orange Kloof; Oct.

4. Rhoicissus tomentosa (= R.capensis). VITACEAE. *Wild Vine, Bosdruif, Monkey Rope, Bobbejaantou.* Woody climber; abundant in eastern kloofs on Table Mountain and Devil's Peak; Nov.-Jan.; the leaves turn red before falling.

5. Curtisia dentata (= C. faginea). CORNACEAE. *Assegai, Assegaai.* Tree; up to 9 m; occasional – forests, kloofs; Jan.-Feb.

6. Brabejum stellatifolium. PROTEACEAE. *Wild Almond, Cape Almond, Wilde amandel.* Large shrub, or small tree; up to 4,5 m; locally abundant on east side of Table Mountain; Dec.-Jan.; forms Van Riebeeck's boundary hedge on Wynberg Hill.

Scale: one-third life size

Damp Places Near The Sea

1. **Grammatotheca bergiana.** CAMPANULACEAE. Low, straggling; up to 300 mm; occasional in damp places in the north; Dec.-Apr.; differs from *Lobelia* in having a one-chambered ovary.

● 2. **Nidorella foetida.** ASTERACEAE (= COMPOSITAE). Up to 300 mm; rather rare, swampy places – Chapman's Bay and Muizenberg; Jan.-Dec.

3. **Hebenstreitia cordata.** SELAGINACEAE. Much-branched woody perennial; up to 500 mm; occasional in sand near the sea; Nov.-May.

4. **Scirpus nodosus.** CYPERACEAE. Up to 800 mm; frequent in sandy places, sea shore; Dec.-Mar.

5. **Putterlickia pyracantha.** CELASTRACEAE. Rigid shrub; up to 3 m; occasional; frequent in sand on west coast; Oct.-Dec.; fruit Feb.

6. **Solanum americanum** (= S. quadrangulare). SOLANACEAE. Straggling; occasional on sandy flats in the north; usually Dec.-Feb.

7. **Limonium scabrum.** PLUMBAGINACEAE. *Sea Lavender, Papierblom.* Frequent in sandy soil near the sea; Dec.-Feb.

8. **Lobelia anceps.** LOBELIACEAE (= CAMPANULACEAE). Prostrate; frequent in wet places; Dec.-June.

◆ 9. **Samolus valerandi.** PRIMULACEAE. *Brookweed.* Erect; up to 300 mm; pale green glabrous annual; locally frequent in marshes; Nov.-Feb. A doubtful native.

Scale: life size

1. **Roella decurrens.** CAMPANULACEAE. Annual; up to 500 mm; local, east slopes of Table Mountain, Kirstenbosch cleared area; Jan.-Mar.

2. **Erica hirtiflora.** ERICACEAE. Shrublet; up to 800 mm; common on mountain slopes and in marshes; Jan.-Apr., but later at high altitudes; shape of flowers variable. (See also p. 192).

3. **Erica nudiflora.** ERICACEAE. Low, scrambling; 150-300 mm; frequent on hill slopes; Feb.-June.

4. **Campylostachys cernua.** VERBENACEAE. Low dense shrublet; 300-600 mm; frequent on north and west slopes of Table Mountain; Feb.-Apr.

5. **Roella triflora.** (= R.dregeana). CAMPANULACEAE. Erect; 150-500 mm; frequent, especially in the south; Dec.-Mar.

6. **Phylica imberbis.** RHAMNACEAE. Shrub; 300-500 mm; frequent; usually Dec.-Mar.

7. **Helichrysum helianthemifolium** (= H.capitellatum). ASTERACEAE (= COMPOSITAE). Straggling shrublet; up to 1,2 m; occasional in northern area; Nov.-Mar.; the leaves have 3 distinct veins.

8. **Serruria fasciflora** (= S.burmannii). PROTEACEAE. *Spinnekopbos.* 500 mm – 1 m; frequent; flats and lower slopes; June-Feb.

9. **Drimia media.** HYACINTHACEAE (= LILIACEAE). 300-500 mm; occasional, on hill slopes; Jan.-Mar.

10. **Lobelia setacea.** LOBELIACEAE (= CAMPANULACEAE). Straggling; frequent; Nov.-Apr.; a marsh form.

11. **Roella squarrosa.** CAMPANULACEAE. Usually prostrate; frequent on mountains; Dec.-Mar.

Scale: life size

1. **Gladiolus brevifolius.** IRIDACEAE. *Pypie.* 200-600 mm; common on flats and mountain slopes, especially in the south; Feb.-May, before the leaves appear.

2. **Erica ericoides** (= Blaeria ericoides.) ERICACEAE. Shrub; up to about 1,2 m; frequent on rocky slopes and on the southern flats; Jan.-May; sweet-scented.

3. **Dianthus albens.** CARYOPHYLLACEAE. 150-500 mm; occasional, at low altitudes; usually Nov.-Dec.

4. **Tenicroa filifolia** (= Urginea flexuosa). HYACINTHACEAE (= LILIACEAE). 300-500 mm; occasional, on damp heaths at low altitudes, especially in the south; Jan.-Feb.

● 5. **Staavia dodii.** BRUNIACEAE. Shrublet; up to 600 mm; occasional on rocky ridges between Rooihoogte and Brightwater; usually Apr.-Sept.

6. **Tritoniopsis parviflora** (= Exohebea parviflora). IRIDACEAE. 150-300 mm; frequent on mountain slopes and in peat on flats and plateaux; Nov.-Feb.

7. **Lampranthus emarginatus.** MESEMBRYANTHEMACEAE. Erect; 150-300 mm; common in lay or sand; Nov.-Feb.; very variable. (See also p. 192).

8. **Roella prostrata.** CAMPANULACEAE. Prostrate or straggling; occasional on flats; Dec.-Apr.; both white and blue forms occur.

Scale: life size

1

2

X 10

3

4

5

6

7

8

Mountains and Mountain Slopes

1. **Herschelianthe graminifolia** (= Herschelia graminifolia). ORCHIDACEAE. *Blue Disa, Blou Disa.* 300-600 mm; frequent high on Table Mountain and Muizenberg Mountain; Feb.-Mar.

2. **Disa ferruginea.** ORCHIDACEAE. *Cluster Disa.* 200-500 mm; fairly frequent on rocks on mountains; Feb.-Apr.; flowers appear before leaves.

3. **Gladiolus monticola.** IRIDACEAE. 500-800 mm; frequent on the summit of Table Mountain and Devil's Peak; Jan.-Mar.

4. **Roella muscosa.** CAMPANULACEAE. Prostrate; frequent on the upper plateau of Table Mountain; Jan.-Feb.

5. **Erica curvirostris.** ERICACEAE. 150-500 mm; rather rare on Table Mountain and Constantiaberg at high altitudes; Feb.-May.

6. **Erica abietina.** ERICACEAE. 500 mm-1 m; frequent on Table Mountain and Devil's Peak ; flowers throughout the year; this species is erroneously named *E. coccinea* in the *Flora Capensis.*

7. **Erica brachialis.** ERICACEAE. 500 mm-1 m; occasional, near Llandudno, Chapman's Peak and Cape Point; Jan.-Feb.; the flowers are hairy inside.

8. **Erica pubescens.** ERICACEAE. 150-600 mm; occasional on hillsides mostly in northern areas; Jan.-Apr.

9. **Erica nevillei.** ERICACEAE. Scrambling; 300-500 mm; high mountain summits – Noordhoek Peak Jan.-Mar., Kalk Bay Mar.-June; plants from these two localities differ very slightly, but they can scarcely be separated as species.

Scale: life size

1. **Bulbine favosa.** ASPHODELACEAE (= LILIACEAE). 150-300 mm; common; Feb.-July.

2. **Ornithogalum niveum** (= O. schlechterianum). HYACINTHACEAE (= LILIACEAE). 100-200 mm; frequent on rock ledges in shade over 310 m; Dec.-Feb.

3. **Senecio bipinnatus.** ASTERACEAE. (= COMPOSITAE). Shrublet; about 600 mm; frequent on mountain slopes from Table Mountain to Constantiaberg; Nov.-Feb.

4. **Bobartia indica.** IRIDACEAE. *Biesroei.* 500-800 mm; very common on mountain slopes, especially after fires; Oct.-Mar., leaves very slender and tough, 1-2 m long.

5. **Erica lutea.** ERICACEAE. *Geelrysheide.* 300-500 mm; frequent on high mountain slopes; Feb.-July. Both yellow and white forms occur.

6. **Gibbaria ilicifolia.** ASTERACEAE (= COMPOSITAE). Sticky shrublet; up to 1 m; frequent on Table Mountain; Aug.-Mar.

7. **Cyclopia galioides.** FABACEAE (= LEGUMINOSAE). Shrublet; up to 1 m; occasional on flats and hills in the south; Jan.-May.

8. **Arctotis aspera.** ASTERACEAE (= COMPOSITAE). Harsh shrublet; up to 1m; occasional on hill slopes; May-Feb.

Scale: life size

1

2

3

4

5

6

7

8

X 2

1. **Erica cerinthoides.** ERICACEAE. *Rooihaartjie.* 500 mm-1 m; often dwarfed by burning; frequent on flats and mountain slopes; July-Apr.; flowers very sticky.

2. **Erica viscaria** var. **decora** (= Erica decora). ERICACEAE. *Klokkies-heide.* Up to 600 mm; frequent, particularly in the south; Jan.-May.

3. **Lachenalia rubida.** HYACINTHACEAE (= LILIACEAE). *Sandkalossie, Rooiviooltjie.* 40-250 mm; frequent, usually at low altitudes; Mar.-June.

4. **Erica mammosa.** ERICACEAE. 500 mm-1 m; Dec.-Apr.; very variable in colour – dark red, greenish-cream, reddish-orange and various shades of pink. (See also p. 90).

5. **Alciope tabularis.** ASTERACEAE (= COMPOSITAE). Shrublet; up to 800 mm; frequent on mountain slopes; usually flowers in summer, especially after fires.

6. **Nerine sarniensis.** AMARYLLIDACEAE. *Guernsey Lily, Rooi Nerina.* 300-600 mm; occasional on rocky mountain ledges; Mar.-May; leaves strap-shaped.

7. **Tritoniopsis dodii** (= Exohebea dodii). IRIDACEAE. 150-500 mm; frequent in sandy and rocky places from Red Hill to Cape Point; Jan.-Apr.

8. **Syncarpha canescens** (= Helipterum canescens). ASTERACEAE (= COMPOSITAE). *Everlasting, Sewejaartjie.* Straggling shrublet; up to 300 mm; frequent; Nov.-July; flowers are more or less everlasting.

● 9. **Ursinia tenuifolia.** ASTERACEAE (= COMPOSITAE). Creeping, in damp places, especially in the south; June-Mar.

10. **Erica plukenetii.** ERICACEAE. *Hangertjies.* 300-600 mm; common on hill slopes; Mar.-Sept.; a white form occurs near Simonstown in the Klawer Valley.

11. **Leucadendron salignum.** (= L.adscendens). PROTEACEAE. *Geelbos.* Female; shrublet, 300 mm -1 m; common on flats and mountains; Mar.-Aug.; male and female flowers are borne on separate plants; leaves tinged with red.

Scale: two-thirds life size

1. **Stoebe cinerea.** ASTERACEAE (= COMPOSITAE). Shrub; up to 1,2 m; frequent on eastern slopes; Mar.-May. (See also p. 92).

2. **Eriospermum nanum.** ERIOSPERMACEAE (= LILIACEAE). 150-500 mm; common on hillsides, also occurs at Tokai and Bergvliet; Mar.-Apr.; leaves appear from May; leaf blades heart-shaped, prostrate.

● 3. **Drimia minor** (= Urginea pygmaea). HYACINTHACEAE (= LILIACEAE). 50-100 mm; locally plentiful on Rondebosch Common; Feb.-Apr.; leaves appear from May to June.

4. **Erica subdivaricata.** ERICACEAE. Erect bush; 150-500 mm; rather frequent on flats; Jan.-May.

● 5. **Disa salteri.** ORCHIDACEAE. 150-300 mm; occasional at low levels on recently burnt areas south of Smitswinkel; Apr.-May; leaves appear later, inconspicuous.

6. **Witsenia maura.** IRIDACEAE. *Bokmakierie, Waaiertjie.* Shrublet; up to 2 m; local in marshy ground, Patrys Vlei and near Smitswinkel; Apr.-June.

7. **Phylica plumosa.** RHAMNACEAE. *Featherhead, Veerkoppie.* Shrublet; up to 500 mm; occasional, Lion's Head to Llandudno; May-Aug.

Scale: life size

1. **Amaryllis belladonna.** AMARYLLIDACEAE. *Belladonna Lily, March Lily, Maartlelie.* 500-800 mm; frequent on lower slopes; Feb.-Apr.

2. **Brunsvigia orientalis.** AMARYLLIDACEAE. *Candelabra Flower, Koningskandelaar.* About 500 mm; locally common in sandy places near the sea; Feb.-Mar.

3. **Haemanthus rotundifolius.** AMARYLLIDACEAE. *April Fool, Velskoenblaar.* 150-200 mm; common; Feb.-Mar.; 2 leaves – large, opposite, almost circular. *H .coccineus* differs in having longer leaves.

4. **Boophane guttata.** AMARYLLIDACEAE. *Seeroogblom.* 200-300 mm; common on flats and hills; flowers mainly after fires; Mar.-Apr.; leaves prostrate, fringed with hairs.

Scale: one-third life size

1

2

3

4

1. **Rhus laevigata** var. **laevigata** (= Rhus mucronata). ANACARDIACEAE. *Kraaibessie.* Shrub; up to 2 m; common; June-Nov.; fruit Mar.; often hybridises with other species.

2. **Sideroxylon inerme** (= Calvaria inermis). SAPOTACEAE. *White Milkwood, Witmelkhout, Jakkalsbessie.* Tree; up to 4 m; abundant on sand dunes along west coast; Mar.-June.

3. **Tarchonanthus camphoratus.** ASTERACEAE (= COMPOSITAE). *Camphor Bush, Kanferhout, Vaalbos, Basterysterhoud.* Aromatic shrub or tree; occasional on slopes; Dec.-Mar.; male and female flowers borne on different plants, female illustrated.

4. **Olea capensis.** OLEACEAE. *Ironwood, Ysterhout.* Shrub or tree; up to 12 m; occasional in forests; Nov.-Mar.; pale grey bark; distinguished from *Cassine peragua* (p. 72) in having only 2 stamens.

5. **Chionanthus foveolatus** (= Linociera foveolata). OLEACEAE. *Bastard Ironwood.* Tree up to 9 m; occasional in forests, near the sea; Mar.-June; grey, closely furrowed bark.

6. **Euclea racemosa.** EBENACEAE. *Sea Guarri, Seeghwarrie.* Shrub; up to 4m; abundant on sandhills; Mar.-June; male and female flowers borne on different plants, female illustrated.

7. **Kedrostis nana.** CUCRBITACEAE. *Dawidjieswortel.* Frequent at low altitudes, climbing on bushes; Feb.-Mar.; it has strong odour of carbon bisulphide.

8. **Maytenus oleiodes** (= Gymnosporia laurina). CELASTRACEAE. Stout shrub or small tree; up to 6 m; common among rocks and edges of forests; Mar.-Aug.

9. **Rhus angustifolia.** ANACARDIACEAE. Shrub; up to 4 m; frequent in moist or sheltered places; flowers Oct.-Dec.; fruit Mar.

Scale: two-thirds life size

Forests and Bushy Places

◆ **1. Clematis brachiata.** RANUNCULACEAE. *Klimop.* Woody climber; rare in Constantia Valley; Mar.-Apr.

2. Knowltonia vesicatoria. RANUNCULACEAE. *Brandblaar.* Up to 600 mm; frequent in shade; usually flowers July-Sept.

3. Halleria lucida. SCROPHULARIACEAE. *Witolyf, Tree Fuchsia, Notsung.* Large shrub or small tree; up to 11 m; frequent in forests on mountain slopes; usually May-Sept.

4. Kiggelaria africana. FLACOURTIACEAE. *Wild Peach, Spekhout, Vaderlandsrooihout.* Tree up to 10 m; common in kloofs and sheltered places; usually Oct.-Nov.

5. Virgilia oroboides. FABACEAE (= LEGUMINOSAE). *Keurboom.* Tree; frequent on hillsides and in woods and thickets; Jan.-Apr.

6. Clutia pulchella. EUPHORBIACEAE. A laxly branched shrub; up to 3 m; frequent in ravines on lower slopes; Mar.-Oct.

7. Maytenus heterophylla (= Gymnosporia buxifolia). CELASTRACEAE. *Lemoendoring, Pendoring, Gifdoring.* Stout shrub; up to 3 m; frequent in bushy places; Oct.-Dec.; fruit Mar.; sweet-scented.

Scale: two-thirds life size

1. **Canthium inerme (=** C. ventosum). RUBIACEAE. *Cape Date.* Tree; 3-8 m; occasional on hill slopes – Blinkwater, Platteklip, Skeleton Gorge, Kirstenbosch; flowers Oct.-Nov.; fruit Mar.

2. **Olea europaea** subsp. **africana** (= O. africana). OLEACEAE. *Wild Olive, Olienhout.* Small tree; up to 5 m; frequent on lower slopes near forests, among rocks; Oct.-Mar.

3. **Cunonia capensis.** CUNONIACEAE. *Butterspoon Tree, Rooiels.* Tree; up to 12 m; frequent in mountain kloofs; Mar.-May.

4. **Widdringtonia nodiflora** (= W. cupressoides). CUPRESSACEAE. *Bergsipres, Sapree, Cypress, Bobbejaankers.* Erect shrub; up to 3 m; local on sheltered mountain slopes, frequent on Table Mountain and Karbonkelberg; Jan.-May.

5. **Lichtensteinia lacera.** APIACEAE (= UMBELLIFERAE). *Kalmoes.* 500 mm-1,25 m; frequent, often in shade; Jan.-Mar.

Scale: one-third life size

Shady Places

1. **Kniphofia uvaria.** ASPHODELACEAE (= LILIACEAE). *Red Hot Poker, Vuurpyl.* 400-900 mm; occasional on damp slopes and in marshy places; Oct.-Apr.

2. **Asclepias fruticosa.** ASCLEPIADACEAE. *Gansies, Tontel, Wild Cotton, Wilde Kapok.* Shrub; 900 mm-1,5 m; occasional in damp places at low altitudes, Orange Kloof and southwards, rarely on roadsides; Nov.-Apr.

3. **Liparia splendens** (= L. sphaerica). FABACEAE (= LEGUMINOSAE). *Orange Nodding-Head, Mountain Dahlia, Bergdahlia, Geelkoppie.* Shrub; up to 900 mm; occasional on hill and mountain slopes and by streams; Nov.-Apr.

4. **Moraea ramosissima.** IRIDACEAE. 500-900 mm; locally common, often in damp semi-shade in the northern areas; usually Sept.-Dec.

5. **Chasmanthe aethiopica.** IRIDACEAE. *Suurkanol, Suurknol.* 400-800 mm; occasional under trees and damp places on mountain slopes and plateaux; Apr.-June.

Scale: one-third life size

1

2

3

4

5

1. **Senecio burchellii.** ASTERACEAE (= COMPOSITAE). Up to 500 mm; abundant; Jan.-Dec.

2. **Othonna quinquedentata.** ASTERACEAE (= COMPOSITAE). Shrub. Up to 1.5m; common on mountain slopes; Jan.-July.

3. **Tulbaghia alliacea.** ALLIACEAE (= LILIACEAE). *Wild Garlic, Wilde Knoflok.* 150-300 mm; locally common on flats and lower sandy slopes; Mar.-Apr.; has strong odour of garlic.

4. **Erica crenata.** ERICACEAE. 300-500 mm; occasional on hill slopes; Jan.-May; very sticky.

5. **Erica tristis** (= Philippia chamissonis). ERICACEAE. Robust shrub; 900 mm-2 m; occasional on flats and hill slopes; Feb.-Apr.

6. **Selago dregei.** SELAGINACEAE. Shrublet; 300-500 mm; frequent; Oct.-May.

7. **Senecio pubigerus.** ASTERACEAE (=COMPOSITAE). Up to 900 mm; common; mostly Jan.-May.

8. **Tribulus terrestris.** ZYGOPHYLLACEAE. *Volstruisdoring, Duiweltjies, Dubbeltjiedoring.* Prostrate annual; frequent by roadsides and on waste ground; Feb.-Apr.; a cosmopolitan weed.

9. **Protasparagus compactus** (= Asparagus compactus). ASPARAGACEAE (= LILIACEAE). Rigid shrublet; 400-600 mm; occasional on flats and hill slopes; usually flowers Nov.-Jan., especially after fires.

Scale: life size

● **1. Eriospermum pumilum.** ERIOSPERMACEAE (= LILIACEAE). Dwarf; local on Rondebosch Common and Kenilworth Race Course; Mar.-Apr.; inconspicuous until the fruiting stage.

2. Psoralea laxa. FABACEAE (= LEGUMINOSAE). Low, trailing, often matted; common on flats and hill slopes; Nov.-Apr.

3. Lobelia setacea. LOBELIACEAE (= CAMPANULACEAE). Straggling, frequent; Nov.-Apr.

4. Plecostachys serpyllifolia (= Helichrysum orbiculare). ASTERACEAE (= COMPOSITAE). *Kooigoed, Vaaltee.* Shrub; up to 900 mm; frequent on seasonally damp flats; Feb.-May.

5. Monopsis lutea (= Parastranthus luteus). LOBELIACEAE (= CAMPANU-LACEAE) *Yellow Lobelia.* 150-500 mm; common; Nov.-Apr. (See also p. 176).

6. Nylandtia spinosa (= Mundia spinosa). POLYGALACEAE. *Tortoiseberry, Skilpadbessie.* Spiny shrub; up to 900 mm; frequent on sandy flats and lower slopes; Apr.-Oct.; fruits edible.

7. Protasparagus rubicundus (= Asparagus rubicundis). ASPARAGACEAE (= LILIACEAE). *Wag-'n-bietjie.* Spiny shrub; 600-900 mm; common on flats and hills; usually Mar.-June, but irregular in flowering; scented; distinguished from *P. africanus* by its spineless flowering branchlets.

8. Macrostylis villosa. RUTACEAE. Shrublet; up to 500 mm; frequent on flats and mountains towards the south; Feb.-Apr.

9. Muraltia ericoides. (= M. neglecta). POLYGALACEAE Shrub; up to 300 mm; occasional; frequent on lower slopes of Devil's Peak and Kenilworth Race Course; usually Aug.-Nov.

10. Thesium scabrum. SANTALACEAE. Erect shrublet; up to 500 mm; occasional on flats and lower slopes; Apr.-Nov.

11. Pseudognaphalium undulatum. (= Gnaphalium undulatum). ASTERACEAE (= COMPOSITAE). Erect perennial; up to 600 mm; occasional; Oct.-May.

12. Berkheya rigida. ASTERACEAE (= COMPOSITAE). Spiny; 300-600 mm; frequent in dry places; Aug.-Apr.

13. Cliffortia hirta. ROSACEAE. Straggling shrublet; up to 600 mm; frequent, mostly in the north; Apr.-Oct.

Scale: life size

1. **Cassine maritima** (= Mystroxylon maritima). CELASTRACEAE.
A rigid shrub; up to 1,8 m; frequent on sand dunes in the south;
Mar.-Aug.

2. **Colpoon compressum** (= Osyris compressa). SANTALACEAE. *Cape
Sumach, Pruimbas, Nantagara.* A shrub; up to 1,5 m; common in bushy
places; Dec.-June.

3. **Lycium ferocissimum.** SOLANACEAE. *Bokdoring.* Straggling shrub; up
to 1 m; occasional in sandy ground at low levels; Apr.-Nov.

4. **Pterocelastrus tricuspidatus.** CELASTRACEAE. *Kershout.* Stout shrub
or very small tree; up to 6 m; common at low levels; abundant,
especially in the south; Apr.-Sept.

5. **Maurocenia frangularia.** CELASTRACEAE. *Hottentot's Cherry,
Aasvoëlbessie.* A rigid shrub; up to 4 m; frequent in kloofs and near the
sea; Jan.-May; dark scaly bark.

6. **Cassine peragua** (= C. capensis). CELASTRACEAE. *Lepelhout.* Tree; up to
11 m; frequent in forests; Jan.-May; smooth red or purplish bark.
Distinguished from *Olea capensis* (p. 60) in having 5 stamens.

7. **Cynanchum obtusifolium.** ASCLEPIADACEAE. Climbing; frequent in
coastal – 'bush', occasional at higher altitudes; Jan.-Dec.

8. **Myrica cordifolia.** MYRICACEAE. *Glashout, Waxberry, Wasbessie.* Usually
prostrate shrub; common on stable sand dunes; Apr.-July; in fruit.

Scale: life size

1. **Stoebe fusca.** ASTERACEAE (= COMPOSITAE). Wiry shrublet; up to 300 mm; frequent; Mar.-May.

2. **Stoebe capitata.** ASTERACEAE (= COMPOSITAE). Shrublet; up to 500 mm; occasional on flats and hill slopes; Dec.-Apr.

3. **Disparago lasiocarpa.** ASTERACEAE (= COMPOSITAE). Straggling shrublet; up to 300 mm; frequent; Nov.-Apr.

4. **Indigofera filifolia.** FABACEAE (= LEGUMINOSAE). Shrub; 800 mm-1,5 m; occasional by streamsides on hills and mountains; Feb.-Apr.

5. **Drimia elata.** HYACINTHACEAE (= LILIACEAE). *Jeukbol*. 300-900 mm; frequent in sand at low levels, occasional at higher altitudes; Feb.-Apr.; leaves May, withering Dec.

6. **Eriospermum lanceifolium.** ERIOSPERMACEAE (= LILIACEAE). 300-500 mm; frequent on flats and hill slopes, often in pine woods; Mar.-Apr.; leaves thick, lance-shaped, appearing in May.

7. **Diosma hirsuta** (= D. vulgaris). RUTACEAE. *Kanferbos, Wild Buchu*. Straggling or erect shrublet; up to 1 m; common on flats and mountains; Feb.-Sept.; aromatic.

8. **Gnidia pinifolia.** THYMELAEAECEAE. Shrublet; 150-500 mm; common; Apr.-Nov.

9. **Rhynchosia capensis.** FABACEAE (= LEGUMINOSAE). Prostrate or climbing; frequent; usually Sept.-Jan.

10. **Diosma oppositifolia.** RUTACEAE. Erect shrublet; up to 1 m; frequent on sandy flats and mountains; Feb.-Sept.; aromatic.

11. **Crassula flava.** CRASSULACEAE. 150-500 mm; perennial; frequent; usually Dec.-Feb.

12. **Rafnia angulata.** FABACEAE (= LEGUMINOSAE). *Veldtee*. Shrublet; 300-500 mm; frequent; Sept.-Apr.

13. **Haplocarpha lanata.** ASTERACEAE (=COMPOSITAE). Up to 150 mm; frequent on mountain slopes; Mar.-June, especially after fires.

Scale: life size

1. **Orbea variegata** (= Stapelia variegata). ASCLEPIADACEAE. *Carrion Flower, Aasblom*. Succulent; 60-150 mm; occasional on granite slabs on the northern slopes of Table Mountain, Lion's Head, Llandudno and Simonstown; Feb.-July; flower has a foetid odour.

2. **Adromischus hemisphaericus** (= Cotyledon hemisphaerica). CRASSULACEAE. 150-300 mm; local, Lion's Head and Oranjezicht; Jan.-Apr.

3. **Crassula rupestris** subsp. **rupestris.** CRASSULACEAE. Perennial; up to 250mm; rather rare on rocky slopes; Feb.-Apr.

4. **Asclepias cancellata** (= A. pubescens). ASCLEPIADACEAE. *Wild Cotton, Katoenbos*. Rigid shrub; up to 1,3 m; occasional on slopes; Mar.-Oct.

5. **Euphorbia caput-medusae.** EUPHORBIACEAE. *Noordpol, Vingerpol*. Succulent, the branches forming a cushion-like mass 200-300 mm high, 600-900 mm across; local on lower western slopes from Lion's Head to Cape Point; Apr.-Sept.

Scale: life size

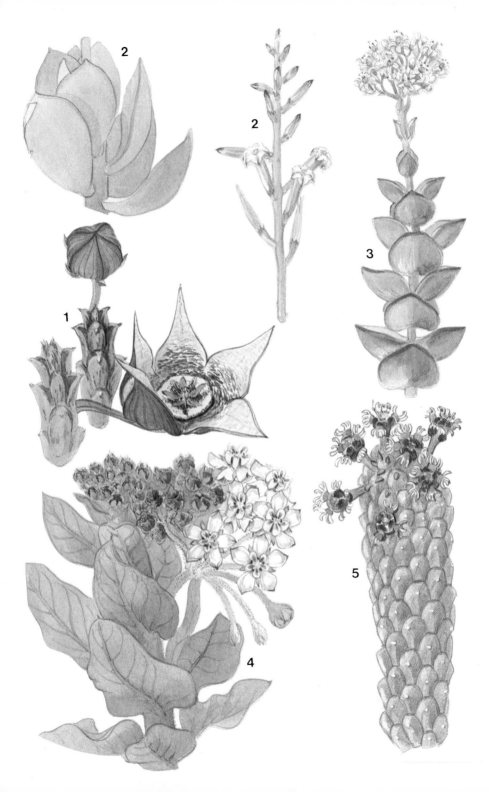

1. **Carpolyza spiralis** (= C.tenella). AMARYLLIDACEAE. 100-200 mm; locally common on flats near Fish Hoek, also on Lion's Head; May-July.

2. **Felicia tenella.** ASTERACEAE (= COMPOSITAE). Erect or prostrate annual; common; usually Sept.-Feb.

3. **Monsonia emarginata** (= M.ovata). GERANIACEAE. *Dysentery Herb, Keitabossie.* Straggling herb; 150-300 mm; local on the western slopes of Devil's Peak; Jan.-Aug.

4. **Myrsine africana.** MYRSINACEAE. *Mirting, Vliekbossie.* Erect shrub; up to 1 m; frequent on sheltered slopes; flowers almost throughout the year.

5. **Thesium capitatum.** SANTALACEAE. Shrublet; up to 300 mm; frequent; Jan.-Dec.

6. **Disperis capensis.** ORCHIDACEAE. *Moederkappie.* 150-350 mm; occasional, heathy places from flats to mountain tops; May-Sept.

7. **Crassula capensis.** CRASSULACEAE. *Cape Snowdrop.* Tuberous; frequent on northern slopes; May-Aug.

8. **Spiloxene minuta.** AMARYLLIDACEAE. 20-50 mm; occasional on low heaths – Rondebosch Common and Kenilworth Race Course; Apr.-June.

9. **Hessea cinnamomea** (= Periphanes cinnamomea). AMARYLLIDACEAE. 150-300 mm; occasional on flats at Kenilworth and Fish Hoek; May-June; leaves appear later.

● 10. **Strumaria tenella** (= Hessea tenella). AMARYLLIDACEAE. 100-200 mm; locally common – Rondebosch Common, Green Point Common, and Fish Hoek flats; May-June.

11. **Homeria collina** (= H. breyniana). IRIDACEAE. *Tulp.* 150-500 mm; common; May-Oct.

12. **Babiana villosula** (= B. hiemalis). IRIDACEAE. *Bobbejaantjie.* 80-200 mm; frequent, as far south as Fish Hoek; May-July.

Scale: life size

1. **Trachyandra brachypoda** (= Anthericum brachypodum).
   ASPHODELACEAE (= LILIACEAE). 150-800 mm; frequent in sandy soils;
   Dec.-May.
2. **Polygala recognita.** POLYGALACEAE. Usually erect; up to 300 mm;
   frequent in sandy places at low altitudes; usually Sept.-Dec.
3. **Romulea flava** (= R. bulbocodioides). IRIDACEAE. Common in grassy
   places; May-Aug.; Cream and yellow forms also occur. (See p. 98).
4. **Rhus rosmarinifolia.** ANACARDIACEAE. Straggling shrublet; up to
   800 mm; occasional on dry slopes; usually July-Sept.; most freely after
   fires.
5. **Indigofera brachystachya.** FABACEAE (= LEGUMINOSAE). Shrublet;
   300-600 mm; occasional in the southern areas, common on Elsie's
   Peak; May-June.
6. **Adenandra uniflora.** RUTACEAE. *China Flower, Kommetjie-teewater.*
   Shrub; up to 500 mm; frequent on slopes near the coast; Apr.-Nov.
7. **Heliophila scoparia.** BRASSICACEAE (=CRUCIFERAE). Erect shrublet; up
   to 800 mm; occasional on lower slopes; May-Sept.
8. **Pauridia minuta.** HYPOXIDACEAE (= AMARYLLIDACEAE). Dwarf; locally
   abundant on heaths and flats – Rondebosch Common; Apr.-May.
9. **Podalyria sericea.** FABACEAE (= LEGUMINOSAE). Shrublet;
   500-600 mm; common on flats and hillsides; May-Aug.
10. **Othonna pinnata.** ASTERACEAE (= COMPOSITAE). Tuberous; occasional
    on slopes, frequent above Camps Bay; May-Sept.
11. **Protasparagus capensis** (= Asparagus capensis). ASPARAGACEAE
    (= LILIACEAE). *Katbos.* Rigid prickly shrublet; 300-800 mm; common on
    flats and lower slopes; Apr-June; very sweet-scented.

Scale: life size

Oxalis (Oxalidaceae) Suring

1. **Oxalis bifida.** Common on shady slopes in the northern areas; Mar.-July, also Sept.-Oct.

2. **O. versicolor.** Very common; May-Sept.

● 3. **O. natans.** Aquatic; locally common in pools on Kenilworth Race Course and vicinity; Aug.-Nov.

4. **O. hirta.** Common; Apr.-Aug.; variable in colour.

5. **O. monophylla.** Frequent on Lion's Head and occasional on Rondebosch Common; Apr.-June.

6. **O. tomentosa.** Locally plentiful on Lion's Head ; Apr.-June.

7. **O. punctata.** Common on hill slopes; Apr.-July; somewhat sticky.

8. **O. obtusa.** Common; July-Oct.; a yellow-flowered form occurs on the eastern slopes of Table Mountain and Devil's Peak.

9. **O. glabra.** Common; May-Aug.; a white form also occurs.

10. **O. eckloniana** var. **sonderi.** Very common; Apr.-Aug.; variable in colour.

11. **O. caprina.** Common, often in cultivated ground; Mar.-May.

12. **O. luteola.** Common in sandy places; May-Aug.

13. **O. compressa.** Frequent in the northern areas; June-Sept.; it differs from *O. pes-caprae* (see p. 122) in having flattened leaf stalks.

14. **O. corniculata.** Annual; common in gardens and on waste ground; Jan.-Dec.; a cosmopolitan weed.

15. **O. polyphylla** var. **pentaphylla.** Frequent on hill slopes; Mar.-June; the typical *O. polyphylla,* which is commoner, has only 3 leaflets.

16. **O. purpurea.** Very common; Apr.-Sept.; pink and white forms occur on the western slopes.

17. **O. eckloniana** var. **sonderi.** (This plant is erroneously named *O. purpurea* in the *Flora Capensis*). Very common; Apr.-Aug; variable in colour. (See also No. 10).

18. **O. dentata.** Very common on hill slopes; Mar.-May; formerly confused with *O. livida.*

Scale: two-thirds life size

1. **Gladiolus priorii** (= Homoglossum priori). IRIDACEAE. *Red Afrikaner.* 300-600 mm; occasional among bushes on mountain slopes and plateaux; May.

● 2. **Mimetes hirtus.** PROTEACEAE. 900 mm-1,5 m; occasional in peaty marshes from Steenberg Plateau to the south, locally abundant near Smitswinkel; May-Oct.

3. **Mimetes cuculatus** (= M. lyrigera). PROTEACEAE. *Rooistompie.* 600 mm-1,2 m; frequent especially in the south; usually Sept.-Jan.

4. **Senecio lineatus.** ASTERACEAE (= COMPOSITAE). Shrublet; about 600 mm; occasional on slopes; Mar.-May.

5. **Lasiospermum bipinnatum.** ASTERACEAE (= COMPOSITAE). Rather rare, roadsides; Apr.-May.

6. **Osmitopsis asteriscoides.** ASTERACEAE (= COMPOSITAE). *Swamp Daisy, Belskruie.* Aromatic shrub; 900 mm-1,5 m; frequent in marshes on mountains and on southern flats; usually Aug.-Nov.

● 7. **Leucadendron macowanii.** PROTEACEAE. Shrub; 900 mm-3 m; very local at Smitswinkel; May-June; flowers from male and female plants illustrated.

Scale: two-thirds life size

1   2   3

                                                    7♀

4   5   6   7♂

1. **Muraltia heisteria.** POLYGALACEAE. *Kastybos.* Erect prickly shrublet; 500-900 mm; common; usually June-Oct.; but also at other times.

2. **Lachenalia reflexa.** HYACINTHACEAE (= LILIACEAE). Usually 60-100 mm; frequent in damp low-lying places; May-Aug.

3. **Polygala myrtifolia.** POLYGALACEAE. *Langelier, Septemberbossie.* Erect shrub; up to 2 m; frequent; May-Dec.

4. **Oftia africana.** SCROPHULARIACEAE (= MYOPORACEAE). Scrambling shrub; about 1 m; frequent on flats and hill slopes, particularly in the north; July-May; the outer branches are often prostrate.

5. **Stylapterus fruticulosus** (= Penaea fruticulosa). PENAEACEAE. Low straggling shrublet; frequent on flats and hill slopes; Mar.-Sept.

6. **Penaea mucronata.** PENAEACEAE. Shrublet; 150-500 mm; common on flats and mountains; Mar.-Oct; flowers often dull red.

7. **Amphithalea ericifolia.** FABACEAE (= LEGUMINOSAE). Shrublet; 300-500 mm; common; May-Sept.

8. **Pelargonium capitatum.** GERANIACEAE. Low shrublet; 300-500 mm; common at low altitudes; usually Sept.-Nov.

◆ 9. **Raphanus raphanistrum.** BRASSICACEAE (= CRUCIFERAE). *Wild Radish, Ramnas.* Annual; 100-500 mm; very common in waste places and on roadsides; May-Oct.; native to Europe.

10. **Pelargonium myrrhifolium.** var. **myrrhifolium.** GERANIACEAE. 150-300 mm; very common on flats and mountains; May-Feb.; very variable in the size of the flowers and the lobing of the leaves. (See also p.184).

11. **Indigofera mauritanica.** FABACEAE (=LEGUMINOSAE). Shrublet; up to 300 mm; frequent on hillsides; May-Aug.

Scale: life size

1. **Oxalis multicaulis.** OXALIDACEAE. Local on eastern slopes of Devil's Peak; May-June.

2. **Brachysiphon fucatus** (= B. imbricatus). PENAEACEAE. Shrublet; 500 mm-1 m; rather rare on mountains in the northern areas; May-Sept.

3. **Indigofera cytisoides.** FABACEAE (= LEGUMINOSAE). Shrub; 1 m or more; frequent on hillsides; Mar.-May.

4. **Cassytha ciliolata.** LAURACEAE. *Devil's Tresses, Vrouehaar.* Climbing parasite; very common on lower slopes; mostly Apr.-June.

5. **Commelina africana.** COMMELINACEAE. Prostrate or straggling herb up to 500 mm; very common on lower slopes; mostly Aug.-Nov.

6. **Salvia africana-caerulea** (= S. africana). LAMIACEAE (= LABIATAE). *Wild Sage, Bloublomsalie.* Shrublet; 600-900 mm; common on hill slopes; usually Aug.-Dec.; differs from *S. chamelaeagnea* (p. 188) in that the calyx enlarges in the fruiting stage.

7. **Trachyandra hispida** (= Anthericum hispidum). ASPHODELACEAE (= LILIACEAE). *Veldkool.* Low herb; occasionally on damp flats and lower slopes; mostly Aug.-Sept.; always flowers in May on Signal Hill.

8. **Empodium plicatum.** HYPOXIDACEAE (= AMARYLLIDACEAE). *Autumn Star, Sterretjie.* Common; Apr.-June; differs from *Spiloxene* in that the ovary is underground in the flowering stage.

9. **Polygonum undulatum.** POLYGONACEAE. Low woody shrublet; 150-500 mm; rather rare; Signal Hill and east side of Devil's Peak; Dec.-May.

● 10. **Athanasia capitata.** ASTERACEAE (= COMPOSITAE). Shrublet; up to 800 mm; frequent in the south; usually Oct.-Dec.

11. **Microloma tenuifolium.** ASCLEPIADACEAE. *Wax Twiner, Kannetjies.* Slender, climbing; rather rare on flats and lower slopes in the northern areas; May-Oct.

Scale: life size

1. **Oxalis commutata** var. **concolor.** OXALIDACEAE. Frequent on hill plateaux and marshy places in the south; Apr.-Aug.; corolla tube the same colour as the petals; a smaller plant than *O. commutata.*

2. **Erica mammosa.** ERICACEAE. 500-1 m; common on flats and mountains; Dec.-May; the southern forms are very variable in colour. (See also p. 54).

3. **Erica mammosa.** See No. 2 above.

4. **Erica phylicifolia.** ERICACEAE. Shrub; 600 mm-1 m; frequent on hill and mountain slopes; Sep.-June; flowers sticky.

5. **Stachys aethiopica.** LAMIACEAE (= LABIATAE). Up to 300 mm; frequent on hill slopes; May-Dec.

6. **Erica imbricata.** ERICACEAE. Usually 300-500 mm; very common on flats and mountains; Feb.-Oct. There is a red form on Table Mountain.

7. **Erica coccinea.** ERICACEAE. 600 mm-1 m; frequent on hill slopes; Apr.-Aug.; usually light red or yellow, rarely green.

8. **Manulea cheiranthus.** SCROPHULARIACEAE. Annual; up to 300 mm; common; May-Feb.

9. **Wurmbea hiemalis** (= W. spicata). COLCHICACEAE (= LILIACEAE). *Swartkoppie.* 150-200 mm; frequent in damp places; usually Sept.-Oct. (See also p. 138).

10. **Oxalis flava.** OXALIDACEAE. Frequent on Lion's Head; May-June; probably exterminated elsewhere.

Scale: life size

1. **Stilbe ericoides.** VERBENACEAE. Straggling shrublet; up to 300 mm; frequent on dry heathy flats; May-Sept. (See also p. 56).

2. **Cryptadenia grandiflora.** THYMELAEAECEAE. Shrublet; about 300 mm; frequent, especially in the south; usually Sept.-Nov. See also p. 92.

3. **Phylica stipularis.** RHAMNACEAE. *Hondegesig.* Shrublet; about 500 mm; common; Mar.-June.

4. **Chrysocoma coma-aurea.** ASTERACEAE (= COMPOSITAE). Shrublet; up to 500 mm; frequent; usually Sept.-Nov.; maritime form. (For the typical form see p. 196).

5. **Stoebe cinerea.** ASTERACEAE (= COMPOSITAE). Shrub; up to 1,5 m; frequent on eastern slopes. Mar.-May.

6. **Spergularia,** species unidentifiable. CARYOPHYLLACEAE. (The fruits are necessary for determination).

7. **Euphorbia tuberosa.** EUPHORBIACEAE. 50-80 mm; common in sandy soil on flats and hills; Apr.-Sept.; male and female flowers borne on separate plants, female illustrated.

8. **Erica sessiliflora.** ERICACEAE. *Green Heath, Groenheide.* 150-500 mm; occasional in damp places on mountains and hill sides; Apr.-Sept.

● 9. **Erica clavisepala.** ERICACEAE. Densely bushy; up to 300 mm; occasional in damp, peaty hollows from Smitswinkel southwards; Feb.-May.

10. **Senecio triqueter.** ASTERACEAE (= COMPOSITAE). Dwarf; 150-300 mm; occasional on hill slopes from Muizenberg southwards; Dec.-May.

11. **Senecio crassulifolius.** ASTERACEAE (= COMPOSITAE). Succulent; occasional in rock crevices; Jan-June.

12. **Spiloxene alba.** HYPOXIDACEAE (= AMARYLLIDACEAE). Common in marshes and on wet heaths; May-July.

13. **Spiloxene curculigoides.** HYPOXIDACEAE (= AMARYLLIDACEAE). Frequent on heaths and on slopes in the southern areas; Apr.-May.

14. **Metalasia muricata.** ASTERACEAE (= COMPOSITAE). *Blombos.* Shrub; up to 2 m; very common; Apr.-Sept.

15. **Anaxeton laeve** (= A. asperum). ASTERACEAE (= COMPOSITAE). Low shrublet; common on hills in the south; Apr.-Aug.; buds pink.

Scale: life size

1. **Zaluzianskya capensis** (= Z. dentata) SCROPHULARIACEAE. Annual; up to 500 mm; frequent on mountain slopes; May-Nov.

2. **Eriocephalus africanus.** ASTERACEAE (= COMPOSITAE). *Kapokbossie, Wilde Roosmaryn.* Shrub; up to 1m; frequent on dry western slopes; May-Sept. The illustration on the left shows the fruiting heads.

3. **Struthiola dodecandra.** THYMELAEAECEAE. *Heuningblommetjie.* Shrublet; up to 600 mm; frequent; usually Nov.-Mar.; flowers generally white.

4. **Clutia alaternoides.** EUPHORBIACEAE. Much-branched wiry shrublet; about 1 m; frequent; May-Oct.; male and female flowers borne on separate plants, male flower illustrated; a very variable plant. (Female flower illustrated on p. 106).

5. **Saltera sarcocolla** (= Sarcocolla tetragona). PENAEACEAE. 300-600 mm; frequent on hills and the southern flats where it becomes depauperated; Jan.-Dec.

6. **Stoebe plumosa.** ASTERACEAE (= COMPOSITAE). *Slangbos.* Shrub; 300 mm – 1,2 m; frequent; Apr.-June, also Oct.

7. **Phylica buxifolia.** RHAMNACEAE. Shrub; up to about 3 m; frequent; Apr.-Aug.

8. **Phylica pubescens.** RHAMNACEAE. *Featherhead, Veerkoppie.* Erect shrub; up to 1,2 m; occasional on lower eastern slopes from Table Mountain to Constantiaberg; May-Aug.

9. **Polyxena corymbosa** (= Hyacinthus corymbosus). HYACINTHACEAE (= LILIACEAE). Dwarf; rather rare near the sea coast – Green Point Common, Camps Bay; May-Aug.

10. **Senecio pinifolius.** ASTERACEAE (= COMPOSITAE). Shrublet; up to 300 mm; frequent in sheltered places; usually Dec.-Jan.

Scale: life size

Proteaceae

1. **Protea nitida** (= P. arborea). *Waboom.* 1-3 m; frequent on mountain slopes; mostly Apr.-Aug.

2. **Leucadendron coniferum** (= L. sabulosum). Shrub 1-4 m; locally common from Karbonkelberg to the south; usually Sept.-Oct.; male and female flowers borne on different plants, female, in fruit, illustrated.

3. **Protea coronata** (= P. macrocephala). Shrub; 1-3 m; frequent on mountain slopes from Constantiaberg to the north; Apr.-Aug.

4. **Mimetes fimbriifolius** (= M. hartogii). Stout dense shrub or small tree; up to 4 m; frequent on mountains and on the southern flats; June-Nov.

5. **Protea lepidocarpodendron.** Shrub; 1-2 m; fairly common on exposed slopes; May-Nov.

6. **Protea repens** (= P. mellifera). *Sugar Bush, Suikerbossie.* Shrub; 2-3 m; frequent on mountain slopes, but now nearly exterminated on the Cape Flats; June-Aug.

7. **Leucospermum hypophyllocarpodendron** (= L. hypophyllum). Prostrate stems 300-600 mm; creeping; frequent on sandy flats; usually Aug.-Dec.

8. **Protea speciosa.** Shrub; up to 1 m; occasional on hills and mountains, also on the southern flats; Jan.-Apr., but also at other times.

Scale: one-sixth life size

● **1. Gladiolus bonaespei** (Homoglossum merianellum). IRIDACEAE. *Flames.* 300-600 mm; frequent on flats and hills in the south; May-June.

2. Castalis nudicaulis (= Dimorphotheca nudicaulis). ASTERACEAE (= COMPOSITAE). *Wilde Witmagriet.* More or less erect; frequent; June-Oct.

3. Romulea flava (= R. bulbocodioides). IRIDACEAE. Common in grassy places; May-Aug.; cream and white forms in the south; flowers at almost any time.(See p. 80).

4. Liparia parva. FABACEAE (= LEGUMINOSAE). Low, scrambling; occasional on flats and hillsides in the south; flowers at almost any time.

● **5. Audouinia capitata.** BRUNIACEAE. *False Heath.* Shrublet; 300-500 mm; rather rare on rocky hills and ridges from Karbonkelberg southwards; May-Oct.

6. Achyranthes sicula. AMARANTHACEAE. *Klits.* 300-600 mm; occasional in shade on lower eastern slopes of Table Mountain; June-Jan.

7. Lobostemon montanus. BORAGINACEAE. Shrub; 1-2m; frequent in bushy places; June-Sept.

8. Trachyandra revoluta (= Anthericum revolutum). ASPHODELACEAE (= LILIACEAE). Common on seasonally damp flats; June-Sept., most freely after fires.

9. Crotalaria capensis. FABACEAE (= LEGUMINOSAE). A robust shrub; 2 m or more; frequent near habitations; June-Dec.; native of Eastern Province.

10. Solanum pseudocapsicum. SOLANACEAE. *Jerusalem Cherry.* Erect shrublet; up to 1 m; locally frequent on lower slopes, on Newlands Avenue; usually Sept.-Nov.

Scale: two-thirds life size

1. **Cliffortia filifolia.** ROSACEAE. Low shrub; 300-600 mm; frequent; May-Aug.

◆ 2. **Persicaria serrulata** (= Polygonum salicifolium). POLYGONACEAE. Sprawling stems 200-600 mm high; on streamsides and in wet ditches; common; Jan.-Dec.

3. **Knowltonia capensis.** (= K. hirsuta). RANUNCULACEAE. Occasional, in bushy places on hill slopes; June-Dec.

4. **Anisodontea scabrosa** (= Malvastrum scabrosum). MALVACEAE. Sticky shrub; up to 1,5 m; frequent in sheltered places in the north; usually Aug.-Nov.

◆ 5. **Spergula arvensis.** CARYOPHYLLACEAE. *Spurry.* Erect or sprawling annual; 100-500 mm; frequent; June-Nov.; native of Europe; a weed of cultivation.

6. **Nemesia macrocarpa.** SCROPHULARIACEAE. *Leeubekkie.* Perennial; up to 500 mm; occasional on mountains in the north; Nov.-June.

7. **Serruria villosa** (= S. vallaris) PROTEACEAE. Erect shrub; 500-800 mm; frequent on hill slopes and the southern flats; Mar.-Oct.

8. **Euryops abrotanifolius.** ASTERACEAE (= COMPOSITAE). *Geelmagriet.* Shrub; up to 1 m; common on hill and mountain slopes; May-Oct.

Scale: life size

1. **Clutia polygonoides.** EUPHORBIACEAE. Shrublet; 300-600 mm; occasional on mountains; as far south as Muizenberg; June-Nov.; male and female flowers borne on separate plants, male illustrated.

2. **Lotononis prostrata.** FABACEAE (= LEGUMINOSAE). Straggling or prostrate; locally frequent on Lion's Head; June-Sept.

3. **Crassula thunbergiana** subsp. **thunbergiana** (= C. zeyheriana). CRASSULACEAE. 50-200 mm; annual; common on sandy flats; June-Sept.

4. **Thesium funale.** SANTALACEAE. Shrublet; 100-500 mm; common; Jan.-Dec.

5. **Osteospermum clandestinum.** ASTERACEAE (= COMPOSITAE). Somewhat sticky to the touch; frequent; June-Oct. (See also p. 148).

6. **Rumex cordatus** (= R. sarcorrhizus). POLYGONACEAE. *Tongblaar.* Erect green or red perennial; up to 600 mm; common; increases after fires; June-Nov.

7. **Montinia caryophyllacea.** MONTINIACEAE. *Peperbos, Bergklappers.* Shrub; up to 1,5 m; common on hill slopes; May-Oct.; male and female flowers borne on separate plants, male illustrated.

8. **Othonna stenophylla.** ASTERACEAE (= COMPOSITAE). Tuberous; frequent in sandy place; June-Sept.

9. **Galaxia fugacissima.** IRIDACEAE. Dwarf; locally common on Signal Hill, Rondebosch Common, Kenilworth Race Course; June-Sept.

● 10. **Leucadendron levisanus.** PROTEACEAE. Shrublet; 500-900 mm; occasional on flats, mostly in the northern area; usually Sept.-Nov.; male and female flowers borne on separate plants, male illustrated.

Scale: life size

1. **Zehneria scabra** (= Melothria punctata). CUCRBITACEAE. Frequent; climbing by tendrils on bushes; usually Mar.-July; male and female flowers borne on separate plants, female illustrated.

◆ 2. **Mercurialis annua.** EUPHORBIACEAE. *Annual Mercury.* Annual; about 300-500 mm; a common weed of gardens and waste places; Jan.-Dec. Introduced from Europe.

3. **Ruschia sarmentosa.** MESEMBRYANTHEMACEAE. Occasional in sand from Clovelly to the south; July-Aug.

4. **Maytenus acuminata** (= Gymnosporia acuminata). CELASTRACEAE. *Sybas.* A tree with smooth dark bark and red slender twigs; 6 m; occasional in forests and mountain kloofs; June-Sept.

5. **Lycium afrum.** SOLANACEAE. Shrub; occasional near the sea; usually Nov.-May.

6. **Androcymbium eucomoides.** COLCHICACEAE (= LILIACEAE). 60-200 mm; locally common on Wynberg Hill and along west coast; July-Oct.

7. **Olinia ventosa** (= O. cymosa). OLINIACEAE. *Hard Pear, Rooibessie, Rooihout.* Tree; up to 10 m; frequent in forests; June-Oct.; fruit red.

8. **Grewia occidentalis.** TILIACEAE. *Kruisbessie, Knoppieshout, Buttonwood.* Shrub; up to 2 m; occasional in sheltered bushy places in the north; usually Sept.-Jan.; fruits yellow to orange.

9. **Rhus tomentosa.** ANACARDIACEAE. Shrub; rarely over 2 m; common in bushy places; usually Oct.-Dec.; often hybridizes with other species.

Scale: two-thirds life size

1. **Tephrosia capensis**. FABACEAE (= LEGUMINOSAE). Low, straggling; frequent on hill slopes; July-Apr.

2. **Viscum capense**. LORANTHACEAE. *Voëlent, Mistel, Mistletoe*. Stems 150-500 mm long; parasitic shrub; found chiefly on *Rhus*; frequent in the south; Jan.-Dec.

3. **Erica hispidula.** ERICACEAE. Shrub; 500-800 mm; frequent in damp places on hills and mountains; Jan.-Dec.

4. **Zygophyllum procumbens.** ZYGOPHYLLACEAE. Sprawling; occasional in the south; frequent near Vasco da Gama Peak; July-Aug.

5. **Lampranthus filicaulis.** MESEMBRYANTHEMACEAE. Branches 30-100 mm; frequent in damp or wet depressions on the Cape Flats; June-July.

6. **Felicia amoena** (= F. pappei). ASTERACEAE (= COMPOSITAE). Perennial, sometimes an annual; frequent; July-Dec.

7. **Myrica quercifolia.** MYRICACEAE. Erect shrub; usually 150-500 mm; common on slopes; occasional on flats; July-Sept,; male and female flowers borne on separate plants.

8. **Agathosma serpyllacea.** RUTACEAE. Aromatic heath-like shrublet; up to 300 mm; occasional on rocky ridges near Hout Bay and in the south; Apr.-Oct.

9. **Clutia alaternoides.** EUPHORBIACEAE. Wiry shrublet; up to 1 m; frequent on flats, hills and mountain slopes; May-Oct.; male and female flowers borne on separate plants, female illustrated. (For male flowers see p. 94).

10. **Liparis capensis.** ORCHIDACEAE. Up to 150 mm; occasional on mountains, more common in the south; May-July.

Scale: life size

1. **Erica baccans.** ERICACEAE. Shrublet; 600-900 mm; rather common on the lower slopes; July-Dec.

2. **Anthospermum galioides** subsp. **galioides** (= A. ciliare). RUBIACEAE. Up to 200 mm; shrublet; rather common; July-Sept.; male and female flowers borne on separate plants, male illustrated.

3. **Hermannia ternifolia**. STERCULIACEAE. Sprawling shrublet; occasional in the extreme south; July-Nov.

4. **Gymnodiscus capillaris.** ASTERACEAE (= COMPOSITAE). Small annual; common in sandy places; June-Oct.

5. **Thesium strictum.** SANTALACEAE. Straggling shrub; up to 2m; occasional on hill slopes; Jan.-Dec.; usually in spring.

6. **Plexipus cernuus** (= Chascanum cernuum). VERBENACEAE. Straggling shrublet; up to 300 mm, occasional on flats from Fish Hoek to the south; July-Sept.

7. **Sebaea exacoides.** GENTIANACEAE. Annual; up to 200 mm; frequent; July-Oct. (See also p. 142).

8. **Hebenstreitia repens.** SELAGINACEAE. Annual; up to 150 mm; frequent; July-Nov.

9. **Lotononis umbellata.** FABACEAE (= LEGUMINOSAE) Low, creeping; occasional on flats and western hillsides in the northern areas; July-Nov.

10. **Oedera prolifera** (= Eroeda capensis). ASTERACEAE (= COMPOSITAE). Shrublet; up to 300 mm; frequent on dry slopes; July-Oct.

Scale: life size

● **1. Xiphotheca fruticosa** (= Priestleya tomentosa). FABACEAE
(= LEGUMINOSAE). *Silver Pea*. Shrublet; 500-800 mm; occasional on
mountain slopes; Apr.-Sept.

2. Lobostemon glaucophyllus x **L. trichotomus.** BORAGINACEAE. A natural hybrid collected in Wynberg Park; Aug.-Nov.; similar hybrids are
frequent on Wynberg Hill.

3. Podalyria calyptrata. FABACEAE (= LEGUMINOSAE). *Ertjiebos, Keurtjie.*
Shrub; 3 m or more; common in kloofs and on hillsides; July-Sept.

4. Dipogon lignosus (= Dolichos gibbosus). FABACEAE (= LEGUMINOSAE).
Wilde-ertjie. Climbing on shrubs; common; July-Jan.

5. Lachenalia aloides (= L. tricolor). HYACINTHACEAE (= LILIACEAE).
Klipkalossie. 150-300 mm; rather local, in rock crevices in the southern
area at Oliphantsbos and near Sirkelvlei; July-Nov. (I am indebted to
Miss W.F. Barker for this drawing).

● **6. Erica patersonia** (= E. abietina of *Flora Capensis*, not of L.).
ERICACEAE. *Mealie Heath, Mielieheide.* Erect shrub; 600 mm or more;
now rare; in marshes from Smitswinkel to the south; Apr.-Aug.

7. Ornithoglossum viride. COLCHICACEAE. (= LILIACEAE). *Slangkop.*
100-200 mm; frequent on sandy flats and on lower slopes; June-Sept.

8. Solanum tomentosum. SOLANACEAE. Straggling shrub; up to 1,5 m;
frequent in dry bushy places; July-Oct.

9. Anemone tenuifolia (= A.capensis). RANUNCULACEAE. *Cape Anemone.*
Up to 600 mm; occasional on mountains above 465 m; June-Sept.

Scale: two-thirds life size

Aquatics and Vlei Plants

● 1. **Apium inundatum.** APIACEAE (= UMBELLIFERAE). Aquatic; local on the Cape Flats, Ottery and Zandvlei; Aug.-Nov.

2. **Drosera trinervia.** DROSERACEAE. *Sonnedou.* Sticky, small, stemless; common in damp places; Aug.-Nov.; flowers rarely reddish purple; the flower stalks usually bear 2 to 9 flowers.

3. **Cotula vulgaris.** ASTERACEAE (= COMPOSITAE). Erect or creeping annual; common in pools and damp places on the flats; mostly July-Sept.

4. **Utricularia bisquamata** (= U. capensis). LENTIBULARIACEAE. *Bladderwort, Blasieskruid.* Insectivorous; up to 100 mm; frequent in damp places; Aug.-Mar.

5. **Cotula coronopifolia.** ASTERACEAE (= COMPOSITAE). *Gansgras.* Erect or creeping annual; common in damp places on the flats; May-Feb.

6. **Romulea tabularis** (= R. duthieae). IRIDACEAE. Occasional in damp places on the Cape Flats; July-Sept.

7. **Triglochin bulbosa.** SCHEUCHZERIACEAE. Common on sandy flats, often in damp places; May-Dec.

8. **Spiloxene aquatica.** HYPOXIDACEAE (= AMARYLLIDACEAE). Common in ditches, pools and vleis; June-Oct.

9. **Limosella grandiflora** (= L. capensis). SCROPHULARIACEAE. Aquatic; variable in size; occasional in pools on the flats; Aug.-Nov.

◆ 10. **Ranunculus trichophyllus.** RANUNCULACEAE. *Water Crowfoot, Water Buttercup.* Aquatic; in pools, Ottery; Aug.-Oct.

11. **Aponogeton angustifolius.** APONOGETONACEAE. Aquatic; occasional in pools, Ottery and Kenilworth; Aug.-Sept.

12. **Crassula natans** var. **natans.** CRASSULACEAE. Erect or straggling annual; common in pools and damp places; July-Oct.

Scale: life size

1. **Moraea vegeta** (= M. juncea). IRIDACEAE. 150-300 mm; locally common in shade at the foot of Table Mountain and from Rondebosch to Wynberg; Aug.-Oct.

2. **Othonna filicaulis.** ASTERACEAE (= COMPOSITAE). Tuberous; variable in size; frequent, often among bushes; June-Aug.

3. **Moraea tripetala.** IRIDACEAE. *Blou-uintjie.* 300-500 mm; frequent on flats and lower mountain slopes; Aug.-Dec. (See also p. 198).

4. **Coleonema album.** RUTACEAE. *Cape May, Klipboegoe.* Woody shrub; 500 mm-2 m; common among rocks and on ledges, usually near the coast; mostly July-Nov.

5. **Hemimeris montana** (= H. racemosa). SCROPHULARIACEAE. Small annual; frequent; July-Oct.

6. **Hermannia multiflora** (= H. cuneifolia). STERCULIACEAE. *Geneesbossie.* Stems sprawling; common; July-Oct.

◆ 7. **Erodium moschatum.** GERANIACEAE. *Heron's Bill.* Annual; up to 300 mm; common on waste ground; June-Oct. Introduced from Europe. (See also p. 154).

8. **Trachyandra ciliata** (= Anthericum ciliatum). ASPHODELACEAE (= LILIACEAE). *Veldkool.* 150-500 mm; occasional in sand on flats and on lower slopes, more common in south; Aug.-Oct.

9. **Wachendorfia paniculata.** HAEMODORACEAE. *Rooikanol* $^1/_2$ size. 150-600 mm; common; July-Nov.; a variable species.

10. **Othonna digitata.** ASTERACEAE (= COMPOSITAE). Tuberous; frequent in sandy places; June-Sept.

Scale: life size

1. **Zaluzianskya divaricata.** SCROPHULARIACEAE. 60-200 mm; annual; occasional on hill slopes; Aug.-Oct.

2. **Agathosma ciliaris.** RUTACEAE. *Bergboegoe.* Up to 400 mm; common on granite or sandstone ridges; June-Nov.

3. **Arctotis acaulis.** ASTERACEAE (= COMPOSITAE). *Gousblom.* Perennial; frequent; July-Aug.

4. **Pterygodium catholicum.** ORCHIDACEAE. *Oumakappie, Mammakappie.* Up to 300 mm; frequent; Aug.-Nov.

5. **Cyphia digitata.** CAMPANULACEAE. *Baroe.* Climbing; occasional in the north; Aug.-Oct.

6. **Disperis villosa.** ORCHIDACEAE. *Moederkappie.* 80-150 mm; frequent in grassy places; Aug.-Sept.

7. **Ursinia anthemoides.** ASTERACEAE (= COMPOSITAE). Erect annual; common, especially in sandy places; Aug.-Dec.

8. **Spiloxene capensis.** HYPOXIDACEAE (= AMARYLLIDACEAE). *Sterretjie.* Common near vleis, by streamsides and on mountain slopes; July-Oct.; very variable in size and colour (yellow or white).

9. **Onixotis punctata** (= Dipidax punctata). COLCHICACEAE (LILIACEAE). *Hanekam.* 150-300 mm; frequent; Aug.-Oct.

Scale: life size

1. **Hermannia althaeifolia**. STERCULIACEAE. Erect; up to 500 mm; occasional among bushes in the north; Aug.-Sept.

2. **Protea scolymocephala**. PROTEACEAE. Shrub; up to 1m; locally frequent on sandy flats; common towards Kommetjie; June-Nov.

3. **Gladiolus gracilis**. IRIDACEAE. *Sandpypie, Pypie.* 300-600 mm; frequent in sandy places; June-Aug.

4. **Babiana ambigua**. IRIDACEAE. *Bobbejaantjie.* Dwarf; common in sandy places; Aug.-Sept.; very variable.

5. **Tetragonia herbacea**. AIZOACEAE. Straggling; local on Signal Hill and at Observatory; June-Aug.

6. **Cyphia bulbosa**. CAMPANULACEAE. *Bergbaroe.* 150-500 mm; common in the north; Aug.-Sept.

7. **Sparaxis grandiflora**. IRIDACEAE. *Wit Kalossie, Botterblom.* 150-500 mm; common; Aug.-Sept.

8. **Babiana disticha** (= B. plicata). IRIDACEAE. *Bobbejaantjie.* 150-300 mm; locally common on Signal Hill and the northern slopes of Table Mountain; July-Aug.

9. **Lachenalia orchioides** var. **glaucina** (= L. glaucina). HYACINTHACEAE (= LILIACEAE). *Wild Hyacinth, Blouviooltjie.* 150-300 mm; occasional on sandy flats and hill slopes in the northern areas; Aug.-Oct.

Scale: life size

1. **Pharnaceum elongatum** (= P. incanum). AIZOACEAE. Erect or straggling up to 120 mm long; very common; July-Dec.

2. **Cyphia volubilis.** LOBELIACEAE (= CAMPANULACEAE). *Bosbaroe.* Climbing; frequent among bushes; Aug.-Sept. (See also p. 124).

3. **Indigofera candolleana** (= I. mauritanica var. hirta) FABACEAE (= LEGUMINOSAE). Erect; up to 600 mm; frequent, usually at high altitudes; Aug.-Feb.

4. **Muraltia,** species not identifiable. POLYGALACEAE.

5. **Helichrysum indicum** (= H. expansum). ASTERACEAE (= COMPOSITAE). Small annual up to 300 mm; very common in dry places; Aug.-Feb.

6. **Troglophyton capillaceum** (= Helichrysum capillaceum). ASTERACEAE (= COMPOSITAE). Small annual up to 300 mm; rare; under bushes – Fish Hoek, Smitswinkel, Hangberg and Lion's Head; Aug.-Oct.

7. **Aizoon sarmentosum.** AIZOACEAE. Straggling; up to 500 mm; occasional on flats; Aug.-Sept.

8. **Ruschia macowanii.** MESEMBRYANTHEMACEAE. 150-300 mm; frequent near the sea; Aug.-Oct.

9. **Petalacte coronata.** ASTERACEAE (= COMPOSITAE). Dwarf; frequent in dry places in the south; June-Oct.

10. **Helichrysum teretifolium.** ASTERACEAE (= COMPOSITAE). Small shrublet; rarely 300 mm; common; Aug.-Nov. (See p. 160).

11. **Senecio hastatus** (= S. hastulatus). ASTERACEAE (= COMPOSITAE). Sticky; up to 500 mm; frequent; mostly July-Oct.

12. **Geissorhiza juncea.** IRIDACEAE. 150-500 mm; frequent in damp peaty soil; Aug.-Oct.

Scale: two-thirds life size

1. **Gladiolus watsonius** (= Homoglossum watsonianum). IRIDACEAE. *Red Afrikaner.* 300-500 mm; occasional among bushes on mountain slopes – Lion's Head to Steenberg, Observatory; June-Aug.

2. **Adenandra villosa** (= A. umbellata). RUTACEAE. *China Flower, Shepherds' Delight.* Shrublet; up to 900 mm; occasional on slopes and summits; Apr.-Dec. (See also p. 150).

3. **Oxalis pes-caprae.** OXALIDACEAE. *Sorrel, Suring.* Very common on roadsides and in grassy places; June-Oct. Native, but a troublesome garden weed.

4. **Drosera cistiflora.** DROSERACEAE. *Doublom.* 100-200 mm; rather common on dry flats and slopes; Aug.-Sept.

5. **Pelargonium triste.** GERANIACEAE. *Kaneelblom.* Flower stalks erect, up to 500 mm; common; Aug.-Nov.; night-scented; the lobes of the leaves are variable in width.

6. **Babiana ringens** (= Antholyza ringens). IRIDACEAE. *Hanekam, Rotstert.* 150-300 mm; occasional in sandy soil on flats and near the coast; July-Sept.

7. **Romulea hirsuta** var. **hirsuta** (= R. rosea var. speciosa). IRIDACEAE. *Froetang, Frutang.* Occasional in sand on flats in the north; Aug.-Sept.

Scale: two-thirds life size

1. **Helichrysum dasyanthum** (= H. maritimum). ASTERACEAE
   (= COMPOSITAE). Straggling shrublet; 300-900 mm; occasional near the
   sea; Aug.-Nov.

2. **Cliffortia ruscifolia.** ROSACEAE. *Steekbossie, Doringbos, Climber's Friend.*
   Prickly shrub; up to 1,5 m; common; Aug.-Oct.

3. **Euphorbia genistoides.** EUPHORBIACEAE. *Pisgoed.* Erect; up to
   300 mm; occasional on hill and mountain slopes; Aug.-Sept.

4. **Hermannia hyssopifolia.** STERCULIACEAE. *Pokkiesblom.* Erect shrub;
   300 mm -1,2 m; common in moist or sheltered places, occasional on
   flats; Aug.-Sept.; lower leaves usually toothed at the tip.

5. **Metalasia cephalotes.** ASTERACEAE (= COMPOSITAE). Woody shrublet;
   up to 600 mm; frequent, especially in the south; Aug.-Feb. Often tinged
   with pink.

6. **Baeometra uniflora.** COLCHICACEAE (= LILIACEAE). 150-300 mm;
   common; Aug.-Sept.

7. **Hermannia grossularifolia** (= H. vesicaria). STERCULIACEAE. Erect
   or sprawling; up to 300 mm; frequent on western slopes in the northern
   areas; Aug.-Sept.

8. **Zygophyllum sessilifolium.** ZYGOPHYLLACEAE. Straggling; frequent,
   especially in the north; July-Sept.

9. **Centella capensis.** APIACEAE (= UMBELLIFERAE). Dwarf; up to 100 mm;
   frequent on slopes in the northern areas; June-Oct.

10. **Lotononis involucrata** subsp. **peduncularis** (= L. peduncularis).
    FABACEAE (= LEGUMINOSAE). Low, creeping; frequent; Aug.-Nov.
    (See also p. 166).

11. **Cyphia volubilis.** LOBELIACEAE (= CAMPANULACEAE). *Bosbaroe.*
    Climbing; frequent among bushes in the northern areas;
    Aug.-Sept. (See also p. 120).

Scale: life size

1. **Schizodium obliquum.** ORCHIDACEAE. Up to 300 mm; occasional in damp places, frequent in the south; Aug.-Sept.

2. **Indigofera angustifolia.** FABACEAE (= LEGUMINOSAE). Straggling shrublet; up to 300 mm; occasional on flats and hillsides, mostly in the south; Aug.-Sept.

3. **Polygala bracteolata.** POLYGALACEAE. Erect or spreading; 150-500 mm; frequent; July-Dec. Hairy forms also occur.

4. **Nemesia barbata.** SCROPHULARIACEAE. Annual; about 300 mm; occasional on mountain slopes; Aug.-Sept.

5. **Indigofera capillaris.** FABACEAE (= LEGUMINOSAE). Prostrate or scrambling; occasional on peaty flats and hill plateaux, Kenilworth Race Course; Aug.-Nov.

6. **Centella macrocarpa.** APIACEAE (= UMBELLIFERAE). Shrublet; occasional at low altitudes; Aug.-Jan.

7. **Lampranthus reptans.** MESEMBRYANTHEMACEAE. *Vygie.* Frequent in sand, on the Cape Flats and the lower slopes; June-Sept.

8. **Thesium viridifolium.** SANTALACEAE. Shrublet; up to 500 mm; frequent on rocky slopes in the south; July-Dec.

9. **Euphorbia erythrina.** EUPHORBIACEAE. *Pisgoed.* Erect, up to 600 mm; frequent on slopes and occasional on flats; June-Oct.

Scale: life size

1. **Arctopus echinatus.** APIACEAE (= UMBELLIFERAE). *Platdoring, Pokkiesdoring.* Perennial rosette herb; frequent; May-Aug.; leaves prostrate; male and female flowers are borne on separate plants, male illustrated.

◆ 2. **Solanum hermannii** (= S. sodomaeum var. hermanii). SOLANACEAE. *Apple of Sodom, Bitter Apple, Gifappel.* A branching shrub up to 1 m; roadsides, occasional in dry bushy places; May-Dec.

3. **Leidesia procumbens** (= L. capensis). EUPHORBIACEAE. Annual; up to 300 mm; frequent on wooded slopes – Table Mountain and Devil's Peak; usually July-Jan.

4. **Bulbine alooides.** ASPHODELACEAE (= LILIACEAE). 150-500 mm; common on lower slopes; May-Sept.

◆ 5. **Physalis peruviana.** SOLANACEAE. *Cape Gooseberry, Pompelmoer, Appelliefie.* Straggling herb up to 1,5 m long; rather local – Claremont, Newlands; May-Nov.; fruit edible; introduced from South America.

◆ 6. **Solanum nigrum.** SOLANACEAE. *Nightshade, Nastergal.* Erect or sprawling; up to 500 mm; usually an annual; frequent; usually Dec.-Feb.; introduced form of the species.

7. **Hibiscus trionum.** MALVACEAE. Erect; up to 500 mm; occasional in damp places; Aug.-Jan.

Scale: two-thirds life size

Vlei Flowers

● **1. Gladiolus quadrangulus** (= G. linearis). IRIDACEAE. 150-300 mm; occasional on damp flats as far south as Fish Hoek; Aug-Oct.

   2. Geissorhiza geminata. IRIDACEAE. Occasional in shallow water and round seasonal pools at Kenilworth and Wynberg; Sept.

   3. Senecio littoreus. ASTERACEAE (= COMPOSITAE). Annual; up to 500 mm; frequent in sandy places on flats; Aug. – Nov.; vlei form. (See also p. 136).

◆ **4. Ranunculus muricatus.** RANUNCULACEAE. *Pepergras.* Annual; 150-500 mm; frequent in damp places; Sept.-Oct.; a native of the northern hemisphere.

   5. Onixotis triquetra (= Dipidax triquetra). COLCHICACEAE (= LILIACEAE). *Vleiblommetjie.* Up to 500 mm; very local, in wet hollows or pools in the Cape Flats, Kenilworth and Ottery; Aug.-Sept.

   6. Aponogeton distachyos. APONOGETONACEAE. *Waterblommetjie, Wateruintjie, Cape hawthorn.* Aquatic; common in pools and ditches; July-Sept.; edible.

Scale: two-thirds life size

1

2

3

4

5

6

1. **Dorotheanthus bellidiformis.** MESEMBRYANTHEMACEAE. *Bokbaaivygie.* Dwarf; annual; plentiful in white sand; Aug.-Sept.

2. **Senecio arenarius.** ASTERACEAE (= COMPOSITAE). *Hongerblom.* Varying in height; annual; frequent on both flats and mountains; Aug-Oct. (See also p. 164).

3. **Amellus asteroides.** ASTERACEAE (= COMPOSITAE). Low shrublet; occasional in sandy places; Sept-Mar.

4. **Zaluzianskya villosa.** SCROPHULARIACEAE. *Drumsticks.* Annual; up to 300 mm; frequent in sandy places on flats; June-Oct.

5. **Senecio elegans.** ASTERACEAE (= COMPOSITAE). *Wild cineraria, strandblommetjie.* Annual; frequent on both flats and mountains; July-Mar. Becomes very succulent when near the sea. (See p. 150).

6. **Microloma sagittatum.** ASCELEPIADACEAE. *Bokhorinkies.* Slender, climbing on shrubs; occasional on flats and lower slopes; July -Sept.

7. **Geranium incanum.** GERANIACEAE. *Bergtee, Vrouebossie.* Straggling; common on flats and hillsides; Aug.-Nov. Both pink and white forms occur.

◆ 8. **Orobanche ramosa.** SCROPHULARIACEAE. *Broomrape.* Up to 200 mm; a parasitic herb; occasional at low altitudes; Sept.-Nov.

9. **Solanum guineense.** SOLANACEAE. Shrublet; up to 800 mm; frequent in Kalk Bay Mountain kloofs, occasional on Karbonkelberg; usually Dec.-May.

10. **Cynanchum africanum.** ASCLEPIADACEAE. *Klimop.* A climber; frequent on sandy flats and lower slopes near the coast; June-Nov.

11. **Babiana tubulosa** var. **tubiflora** (= B. tubiflora). IRIDACEAE. *Bobbejaantjie.* 150 -300 mm; occasional in sand and on flats near the coast; Aug.-Sept.

Scale: two-thirds life size

Sand Dunes and Sandy Places

1. **Arctotis hirsuta.** ASTERACEAE (= COMPOSITAE). A somewhat succulent annual; up to 300 mm; locally frequent, Paarden Eiland and Green Point; Sept.-Dec.

2. **Ferraria crispa** subsp. **crispa** (= F. undulata). IRIDACEAE. *Spinnekopblom, Krulletjie.* 300-600 mm; occasional in sand among rocks near the coast – Milnerton, Lion's Head and Table Mountain; Aug.-Oct.

3. **Conicosia pugioniformis** (= C. communis). MESEMBRYANTHEMACEAE. Up to 150 mm; frequent in white sand; Sept.-Dec.

4. **Homeria flaccida.** IRIDACEAE. *Tulp.* 300-600 mm; low-lying damp areas; Aug.-Oct.

5. **Didelta carnosa** var. **tomentosa** (= D. tomentosa). ASTERACEAE (= COMPOSITAE). Collected near Blouberg; not a Peninsula species, but common up the west coast.

6. **Albuca canadensis.** HYACINTHACEAE (= LILIACEAE). *Soldier-in-the-box, Geldbeursie.* 300-900 mm; common; Sept.-Nov. Originally named *Ornithogalum canadense* by Linnaeus under the mistaken impression that it came from Canada.

7. **Sutherlandia frutescens** var. **incana.** FABACEAE (= LEGUMINOSAE). *Cancer bush, Eendjies, Gansiekeur.* Shrublet; 500-800 mm; occasional in sand, Hout Bay and Muizenberg; Sept.-Dec. The typical *S. frutescens* has green leaves.

8. **Grielum grandiflorum.** ROSACEAE. *Duikerwortel.* Prostrate or straggling; local, in sandy places near Milnerton; Sept.-Nov.

9. **Dimorphotheca pluvialis.** ASTERACEAE (= COMPOSITAE). *Witbotterblom, Cape Daisy.* An erect or diffuse annual; very common; Aug.-Oct.

Scale: one-third life size

1

2

3

4

5

6

7

8

9

Sand Dunes and Sandy Places

1. **Sutera tristis.** SCROPHULARIACEAE. Annual; up to 300 mm; frequent on flats; Sept-Dec; flowers scented at night.

2. **Manulea tomentosa.** SCROPHULARIACEAE. Erect or straggling; frequent; mostly July-Dec.

3. **Senecio littoreus.** ASTERACEAE (= COMPOSITAE). Annual; up to 500 mm; frequent in sandy places on flats; Aug.-Nov. (See also p 130).

4. **Helichrysum patulum** (= H. crispum). ASTERACEAE (= COMPOSITAE). Straggling shrublet; frequent in sandy ground at low altitudes; Sept.-Dec.

5. **Oncosiphon sabulosum** (= Matricaria sabulosa). ASTERACEAE (= COMPOSITAE). Low, straggling, aromatic perennial; occasional near the sea; Sept.-Nov.

6. **Sebaea albens.** GENTIANACEAE. Annual; up to 150 mm; occasional on damp sandy flats in the north; Sept.-Nov.

7. **Salvia africana-lutea** (= S. aurea). LAMIACEAE (= LABIATAE). *Beach salvia, Bruinsalie.* Shrub; 800 mm-1,7 m; frequent; June-Dec.

8. **Zygophyllum flexuosum.** ZYGOPHYLLACEAE. *Spekbossie.* Shrub; up to 900 mm; occasional in sand, usually near the sea, common near Milnerton; July-Oct.

9. **Hermannia pinnata** (= H. ciliaris). STERCULIACEAE. Prostrate; frequent near Milnerton, occasional elsewhere; Sept.-Oct.; sweet-scented.

10. **Chrysanthemoides incana.** ASTERACEAE (= COMPOSITAE). Shrublet about 600 mm; occasional, usually near the sea; June-Oct.; branches spine-tipped; differs from the common and taller *C. monilifera* in having greyer foliage.

Scale: two-thirds life size

1. **Moraea gawleri** (= M. decussata). IRIDACEAE. 150-20 mm; frequent on sandy flats in open places on slopes; Aug.-Sept.

2. **Cyphia incisa.** LOBELIACEAE (= CAMPANULACEAE). *Baroe, Kambro.* 100-200 mm; occasional on flats and low slopes; Sept.

3. **Heliophila pusilla.** BRASSICACEAE (= CRUCIFERAE). Annual; 60-500 mm; common in sandy places; mostly Aug.-Oct.

4. **Geissorhiza aspera** (= G. secunda). IRIDACEAE. 100-500 mm; common on flats and mountain slopes; Aug.-Oct.

5. **Cenia turbinata** (= Cotula turbinata). ASTERACEAE (= COMPOSITAE). *Ganskos.* Annual; 60-400 mm; very common; June-Dec.; native but often a common weed; yellow form less common.

6. **Monopsis debilis** var. **depressa.** (= M. simplex). CAMPANULACEAE. Annual; up to 150 mm; frequent in wet places; Sept.-Feb. (See also p. 210).

7. **Moraea papilionacea.** IRIDACEAE. 100-200 mm; very local form; the flowers open in the afternoon; Aug.-Sept.; the flowers are identical with those of the red form, leaves much narrower and almost hairless. (For the yellow-flowered form see p. 160).

8. **Wurmbea inusta** (= W. spicata). COLCHICACEAE (LILIACEAE). *Swartkoppie.* 150-200 mm; frequent in damp places; usually Sept.-Oct. (See also p. 90).

9. **Gorteria personata.** ASTERACEAE (= COMPOSITAE). Annual; up to 300 mm; occasional; Aug.-Oct.

10. **Pelargomium chamaedryfolium.** GERANIACEAE. Low, sprawling; frequent in sandy places; Sept.-Dec., especially after fires; strongly aromatic.

Scale: life size

1. **Silene clandestina.** CARYOPHYLLACEAE. Annual; 100-400 mm; frequent in sand; Sept.-Nov.; flowers opening in late afternoon.

◆ 2. **Silene gallica.** CARYOPHYLLACEAE. Erect annual; 150-500 mm; common on roadsides; Sept.-Nov.; native of Europe.

3. **Eustegia minuta.** ASCLEPIADACEAE. 40-70 mm; tuberous; occasional on flats and low hills in the northern areas; Aug.-Jan.

4. **Selago fruticulosa.** SELAGINACEAE. Shrublet; up to 300 mm; local, on dry slopes of Signal Hill and Devil's Peak; Sept.-Nov.

5. **Crassula dichotoma** (= Vauanthes dichotoma). CRASSULACEAE. Annual; 50-150 mm; common; Sept.-Nov.

6. **Diascia elongata.** SCROPHULARIACEAE. Small annual; frequent; July-Oct.

7. **Microcodon hispidulum.** CAMPANULACEAE. Annual; dwarf; very local – on Lion's Head; Sept.-Nov.

8. **Lebeckia plukenetiana.** FABACEAE (= LEGUMINOSAE). 300-500 mm; rather local above Sea Point and Camps Bay; Aug.-Dec.; distinguished from other rather similar species by its unjointed leaves.

9. **Heliophila meyeri** var. **meyeri** (= H. dentifera). BRASSICACEAE (= CRUCIFERAE). Annual; 150-500 mm; occasional on sheltered mountain slopes above 330 m, in the north; Sept.-Oct.

10. **Heliophila africana** (= H. integrifolia). BRASSICACEAE (= CRUCIFERAE). *Bloubekkie.* Annual; up to 1 m; frequent in sand; Sept.-Oct.; flowers more commonly blue.

11. **Struthiola striata.** THYMELAEAECEAE. *Katstertjie.* Shrub; up to 1 m; occasional, more especially in the eastern areas; mostly Sept.-Oct.

12. **Dischisma ciliatum** var **ciliatum.** SELAGINACEAE. Annual or perennial; 150-500 mm; common; Aug.-Dec.

13. **Holothrix villosa.** ORCHIDACEAE. 100-250 mm; fairly frequent in shade, on mountains or flats; Sept.-Nov.

14. **Wurmbea monopetala** (= W. spicata var. truncata). COLCHICACEAE (= LILIACEAE). *Swartkoppie.* 150-200 mm; frequent on damp flats and lower slopes; Sept.-Oct. (For typical form see p. 90).

Scale: life size

1. **Moraea tricuspidata** (= M. confusa). IRIDACEAE. 500-800 mm; frequent on the lower slopes from Cape Town to Kalk Bay, common on Wynberg Hill; Sept.-Oct.

2. **Polyarrhena reflexa** (= Felicia reflexa). ASTERACEAE (= COMPOSITAE). Straggliing shrublet; up to 600 mm; frequent on mountain slopes; July-Sept.

3. **Hermannia alnifolia.** STERCULIACEAE. Straggling; occasional; Aug.-Sept.; this form with pale yellow flowers occurs near Camps Bay, flowers usually a deeper yellow.

4. **Oedera genistifolia** (= Relhania genistifolia). ASTERACEAE (= COMPOSITAE). *Peperbos.* Somewhat sticky shrub; about 600 mm; frequent on dry slopes in the north; Aug.-Sept.

5. **Erica calycina.** ERICACEAE. 500-800 mm; frequent on the higher parts of Table Mountain and Constantiaberg; July-Dec.

6. **Adenogramma lichtensteiniana.** AIZOACEAE. Scrambling; frequent among bushes; Aug.-Sept.

7. **Lachenalia fistulosa** (= L. convallariodora). HYACINTHACEAE (= LILIACEAE). *Groen viooltjie.* Up to 400 mm; frequent on mountain slopes; Sept.-Oct.

8. **Polycarena** sp. SCROPHULARIACEAE. Species unidentified.

9. **Sebaea exacoides.** GENTIANACEAE. Annual. Up to 200 mm; frequent; July-Oct. (See also p. 108).

10. **Aspalathus carnosa.** FABACEAE (= LEGUMINOSAE). Erect shrublet; 500 mm-1 m; common on hillsides and ridges, especially in the south; Aug.-Dec.

Scale: life size

● **1. Aspalathus capitata.** FABACEAE (= LEGUMINOSAE). Shrub up to 2,4 m; rather rare; in mountain kloofs – Kalk Bay and in the south; Jan-Dec.

2. Leucadendron xanthoconus. PROTEACEAE. *Knoppiesbos, Geelbos.* Shrub; 1-2 m; common on hill and mountain slopes; Aug.-Sept.; male and female flowers borne on separate plants.

3. Gazania pectinata (= G. pinnata). ASTERACEAE (= COMPOSITAE). *Botterblom.* Frequent at low altitudes; Aug.-Nov. (See also p. 170).

4. Cineraria geifolia. ASTERACEAE (= COMPOSITAE). Prostrate or up to 300 mm; frequent in sheltered places; mostly Aug.-Dec., later at high altitudes; unpleasantly scented.

◆ **5. Myoporum serratum.** MYOPORACEAE. *Manitoka.* A tree introduced from Australia.

6. Diospyros whyteana (= Royena lucida). EBENACEAE. *Wild Coffee, Tolletjie, Swartbas.* Tree; up to 7 m; frequent in forests and kloofs; smooth dark-coloured bark; Apr.-Sept.

Scale: two-thirds life size

1

2♀

2♂

3

4

5

1. **Gladiolus alatus.** IRIDACEAE. *Kalkoentjie.* 150-300 mm; occasional in sandy flats and hill slopes; Aug.-Sept.

2. **Pelargonium lobatum.** GERANIACEAE. Flower stalk up to 500 mm; frequent from Signal Hill to Llandudno; Sept.-Nov.

3. **Aristea spiralis.** IRIDACEAE. 300-600 mm; occasional on hill and mountain slopes; Aug.-Oct.

4. **Othonna ciliata.** ASTERACEAE (= COMPOSITAE). Straggling; frequent on hill slopes in the north; July-Oct.

5. **Silene burchellii.** CARYOPHYLLACEAE. Erect; 300-500 mm; occasional on lower slopes; usually Sept.-Dec.

6. **Moraea angusta.** IRIDACEAE. 150-300 mm; frequent on lower slopes in the northern areas, also Kenilworth Race Course; Sept.-Oct.; easily confused with *M. neglecta*, but paler in colour. (See also p. 196).

7. **Relhania fruticosa** (= R. ericoides). ASTERACEAE (= COMPOSITAE). Shrublet; up to 400 mm; locally frequent in dry places in the north; Sept.-Oct.

8. **Leysera gnaphalodes.** ASTERACEAE (= COMPOSITAE). *Hongertee.* Small shrublet; up to 300 mm; locally frequent from Signal Hill to Devil's Peak; Sept.-Nov.

9. **Gladiolus hyalinus** (= G. confusus). IRIDACEAE. 300-500 mm; frequent on the lower slopes from Devil's Peak to Hout Bay; July-Sept.

Scale: two-thirds life size

1. Gladiolus cunonius (= Anomalesia cunonia). IRIDACEAE.
150-500 mm; occasional on lower mountain slopes and flats and on
sand dunes near the coast;Sept.-Oct.

2. Gerbera linnaei (= G. asplenifolia). ASTERACEAE (=COMPOSITAE).
Frequent; Sept.-June; rarely found in flower except after fires.

3. Gladiolus carinatus. IRIDACEAE. *Sandpypie, Mauve Afrikaner.*
150-600 mm; frequent on sandy flats; July-Sept.; very sweet-scented.

4. Osteopermum clandestinum. ASTERACEAE (= COMPOSITAE). sticky
annual; frequent; June-Oct. (See also p. 102).

5. Arctotheca calendula. ASTERACEAE (= COMPOSITAE). *Cape Weed.* Very
common on roadsides and in waste places; Aug.-Nov.

6. Senecio abruptus. ASTERACEAE (= COMPOSITAE). Annual; up to
300 mm; occasional on flats; Sept.-Nov.

7. Pelargonium myrrhifolium var. **coriandrifolium**. GERANIACEAE.
150-300 mm; very common on flats and mountains; usually July-Feb.;
very variable in the size of flowers and lobing of the leaves.

Scale: two-thirds life size

1. Athrixia crinita (= A. heterophylla). ASTERACEAE (= COMPOSITAE). Small shrublet; about 300 mm; occasional on mountain slopes; Aug.-Jan.

2. Gnidia tomentosa. THYMELAEAECEAE. Shrub; up to 1 m; frequent above 330 m; Jan.-Dec.

3. Adenandra villosa. (= A. umbellata). RUTACEAE. *China Flower, Shepherd's Delight.* Shrub; up to 1 m; occasional on slopes and summits; Apr.-Dec. (See also p. 122).

4. Hesperantha falcata. IRIDACEAE. *Aandblommetjie, Aandblom.* 150-300 mm; frequent in open places; Aug.-Nov.

5. Senecio purpureus. ASTERACEAE (= COMPOSITAE). Up to 1 m; occasional on flats and mountains; usually Dec.-May.

6. Selago quadrangularis. SELAGINACEAE. 150-500 mm; occasional on upper mountain slopes in the north; Sept.-Jan.

7. Dischisma ciliatum var. **ciliatum.** SELAGINACEAE. Annual or perennial; 150-500 mm; common; Aug.-Dec. (See also p. 140).

8. Senecio elegans. ASTERACEAE (= COMPOSITAE). *Wild Cineraria, Strandblommetjie.* Annual; frequent on both flats and mountains; July-Mar.; becomes very succulent when near the sea. (See page 132).

9. Silene undulata (= Melandrium undulatum). CARYOPHYLLACEAE. Sprawling stems 400-800 mm long; frequent in shady places on hill slopes; Sept.-Nov.; deep red flowers also occur.

Scale: two-thirds life size

1. **Pelargonium betulinum.** GERANIACEAE. Shrublet; 300-500 mm; rather common in sandy places; Aug.-Oct.

2. **Babiana ambigua** (= B. plicata). IRIDACEAE. *Bobbejaantjie.* Common in sand; Aug.-Sept. (See also p. 118).

3. **Lachenalia unifolia** var. **wrightii.** HYACINTHACEAE (= LILIACEAE). 150-300 mm; frequent in the south; Sept.-Oct.

4. **Euphorbia mauritanica.** EUPHORBIACEAE. *Geel Melkbos.* Succulent shrub; 1 m or more; local, near the coast at Paarden Eiland and Hout Bay; Aug.-Oct.

5. **Watsonia coccinea.** IRIDACEAE. *Waspypie.* 150-500 mm; frequent on moist sandy flats and mountain plateaux; Sept.-Nov.; especially after fires; can be confused with *W. meriana* which is taller, grows in sand and thin rocky soils and still flowers a number of years after fire.

6. **Cysticapnos vesicarius.** FUMARIACEAE. *Klappertjies.* Climbing; frequent among bushes, especially near the sea; Aug.-Sept.

7. **Melasphaerula ramosa.** IRIDACEAE. *Baardmannetjie.* 200-500 mm; frequent in shade on the slopes of Table Mountain, Lion's Head and Karbonkelberg; July-Sept.

Scale: two-thirds life size

◆ **1. Geranium molle.** GERANIACEAE. *Dove's Foot, Crane's Bill.* Small annual; frequent on roadsides and in waste places; Aug.-Nov.; introduced from Europe; *G. dissectum,* with more deeply lobed leaves, is equally common.

◆ **2. Erodium moschatum.** GERANIACEAE. *Heron's Bill, Herb Robert.* Annual; up to 300 mm; common on waste ground; June-Oct.; introduced from Europe; the lower leaves are more fern-like than those of the specimen on p. 114.

◆ **3. Fumaria muralis** (= F. officinalis). FUMARIACEAE. *Fumitory, Duiwelskerwel.* Straggling or climbing annual; very common on roadsides and in waste places; Aug.-Nov.; introduced from Madeira.

◆ **4. Anagallis arvenis** var. **caerulea.** PRIMULACEAE. *Blue Pimpernel.* Annual; stems up to 400 mm long; common; July-Nov.; introduced from Europe; the red-flowered *Scarlet Pimpernel* is less common.

◆ **5. Stachys arvenis.** LAMIACEAE (= LABIATAE). *Field Woundwort.* 150-300 mm; annual; Jan.-Dec.; introduced from Europe; a weed of cultivation.

6. Romulea rosea var. **australis** (= R. rosea var. parviflora). IRIDACEAE. *Froetang, Frutang.* Very common; Aug.-Sept.

7. Monadenia bracteata (= M. micrantha). ORCHIDACEAE. 150-300 mm; frequent in moist, sandy places; Sept.-Nov.

8. Oxalis lanata var. **rosea.** OXALIDACEAE. Local on upper slopes of Wynberg Hill; Aug.-Sept.; the white-flowered typical form is common.

9. Myrsiphyllum scandens (= Asparagus scandens). ASPARAGACEAE (= LILIACEAE). Climbing to about 1 m; frequent in forests on the east slopes of Table Mountain; Aug.-Oct.

Scale: life size

1. **Gynandriris setifolia.** IRIDACEAE. 100-300 mm; frequent, usually in poor soil; Sept.-Oct. A particularly luxuriant specimen.

2. **Wahlenbergia capensis.** CAMPANULACEAE. Annual; 150-800 mm; frequent in the north; Oct.-Dec.

3. **Felicia heterophylla** (= Charieis heterophylla). ASTERACEAE (= COMPOSITAE). Annual; frequent in sandy ground at low altitudes; Sept.-Oct.

4. **Osteospermum dentatum.** ASTERACEAE (= COMPOSITAE). Up to 600 mm; frequent near Muizenberg, occasional elsewhere; Aug.-Jan.

5. **Nemesia versicolor.** SCROPHULARIACEAE. *Weeskindertjies.* Erect annual up to 500 m; common; Aug.-Nov.; very variable in colour. (See also p. 164, p. 178).

6. **Moraea fugax** (= M. fugax var. longifolia). IRIDACEAE. *Uintjie.* 150-800 mm; common; Sept.-Nov.; one leaf very long, sometimes 1 m.

7. **Pharnaceum lineare.** AIZOACEAE. Stems 200-500 mm long; prostrate or scrambling, herbaceous; frequent on the Cape Flats; mostly Sept.-Nov.

8. **Lampranthus glaucus.** MESEMBRYANTHEMACEAE. Erect; 150-200 mm; frequent in sand on the Cape Flats; Aug.-Oct.

9. **Carpanthea pomeridiana.** MESEMBRYANTHEMACEAE. *Vetkousie.* Sprawling annual; 100-150 mm; common in sand; Sept.-Nov.; leaves 50-100 mm long.

Scale: two-thirds life size

1
2
3
4
5
6
7
8
9

1. **Indigofera incana.** FABACEAE (= LEGUMINOSAE). 150-500 mm; frequent on western slopes in the north; Aug.-Oct.

2. **Erica urna-viridis.** ERICACEAE. Widely branched shrub; 1 m or more; Muizenberg mountain only, above 330 m; mostly in Dec.

3. **Indigofera nitida.** FABACEAE (= LEGUMINOSAE). Low, straggling; frequent on hill slopes in the northern areas; Sept.-Nov.; sometimes with 5 leaflets; differs from *I. psoraloides* (p. 216) in that the hairs on the leaflets lie almost laterally.

4. **Lessertia capensis.** FABACEAE (= LEGUMINOSAE). Low, scrambling; frequent on hillsides mostly in the north; Aug.-Oct.

5. **Podylaria argentea** (= P. biflora). FABACEAE (= LEGUMINOSAE). Shrublet; 300-800 mm; occasional on hillsides; Oct.-Dec.

6. **Crassula fascicularis** (= Rochea subulata). CRASSULACEAE. 150-300 mm; common; Oct.-Dec.; scented in the evening.

7. **Gerbera crocea.** ASTERACEAE (= COMPOSITAE). Frequent at low altitudes; Oct.-Mar. (See also p. 178).

8. **Geissorhiza tenella** (= Engysiphon roseus). IRIDACEAE. 200-400 mm; occasional on sandy flats and mountain slopes; Oct.-Nov.

9. **Gladiolus debilis.** IRIDACEAE. *Painted Lady.* 300-600 mm; frequent on mountain slopes and plateaux, from Constantiaberg to the south; Aug.-Oct.

● 10. **Gladiolus ornatus.** IRIDACEAE. *Pink Bell, Pypie.* 300-600 mm; occasional on damp flats and lower eastern mountain slopes; Aug.-Oct.

Scale: two-thirds life size

1. **Linum quadrifolium.** LINACEAE. *Flax.* Straggling; frequent in damp places on mountains in the north; Oct.-Dec.

2. **Satyrium bracteatum.** ORCHIDACEAE. 80-300 mm; locally common in wet places on flats, occasional on mountains; Aug.-Oct.

3. **Pterygodium volucris** (= Ommatodium volucris). ORCHIDACEAE. 150-300 mm; occasional; Sept.-Oct.

4. **Albuca cooperi.** HYACINTHACEAE (= LILIACEAE). 150-500 mm; common on flats and lower mountain slopes; Oct.-Dec.; differs from *A. canadense* in that bulb scales and leaf bases split into fibres at the top.

5. **Helichrysum teretifolium.** ASTERACEAE (= COMPOSITAE). Small shrublet up to 300 mm; common; Aug.-Nov. (See also p. 120).

6. **Ifloga ambigua** (= I. seriphoides). ASTERACEAE (= COMPOSITAE). Shrublet; 600-900 mm; frequent; Sept.-March.

7. **Moraea papilionacea.** IRIDACEAE. 100-200 mm; frequent in sunny places; Aug.-Oct.; there is also a brick-red form (see p. 138).

● 8. **Lampranthus dunensis.** MESEMBRYANTHEMACEAE. *Vygie.* Compact, creeping; occasional in sand on the Cape Flats; Sept.-Oct.

9. **Syncarpha gnaphaloides** (= Helipterum gnaphaloides). ASTERACEAE (= COMPOSITAE). Woolly shrublet; about 300 mm; frequent on hill slopes; Aug.-Dec.

10. **Lapeirousia corymbosa.** IRIDACEAE. 100-150 mm; locally common on Signal Hill, occasional on sandy flats and lower slopes; Sept.-Nov.

Scale: life size

1. **Holothrix cernua** (= H. squamulosa). ORCHIDACEAE. 150-300 mm; frequent in damp, sandy places; Oct.-Nov.

2. **Torilis africana.** APIACEAE (= UMBELLIFERAE). 150-500 mm; frequent at low altitudes; Oct.-Nov.

3. **Pelargonium hirtum.** GERANIACEAE. Rather succulent; 150-300 mm; local, Lion's Head and Camps Bay; July-Oct.; the old leaf stalks persist on the stem.

4. **Bartholina burmanniana.** ORCHIDACEAE. *Spider Orchid.* 50-200 mm; occasional on hill slopes, rare on Table Mountain; Aug.-Oct.

5. **Erica paniculata.** ERICACEAE. 150-500 mm; frequent on western slopes in the northern areas; Aug.-Oct.

6. **Osteospermum spinosum.** ASTERACEAE (= COMPOSITAE). Sticky shrublet; up to 1 m; local on the dry slopes above Camps Bay; Jan.-Dec.

7. **Stoebe aethiopica.** ASTERACEAE (= COMPOSITAE). Shrublet, up to 600 mm; occasional on hill slopes; mostly Sept.-Nov.

8. **Othonna arborescens.** ASTERACEAE (= COMPOSITAE). Low shrub; occasional on exposed rocks on mountains; June-Oct.

Scale: life size

1. **Nemesia versicolor.** SCROPHULARIACEAE. *Weeskindertjies.* Erect annual; up to 500 mm; common; Aug.-Nov.; very variable in colour. (See also p. 156, p. 178).

◆ 2. **Vicia sativa** subsp. **nigra** (= V. angustifolia). FABACEAE (= LEGUMINOSAE). *Common* or *Wild Vetch.* Climbing; frequent in fields and on hillsides; Aug.-Dec.; introduced from Europe; the ripe pods are black, in *V. sativa,* with rather larger flowers, the pods are light brown.

◆ 3. **Silene gallica.** CARYOPHYLLACEAE. Erect annual; 150-500 mm; common on roadsides; Sept.-Nov.; introduced from Europe. (See also p. 140).

4. **Lobelia erinus.** CAMPANULACEAE. Small annual; common; June-Apr.

5. **Cyanella hyacinthoides** (= C. capensis). TECOPHILAEACEAE. *Raaptol, Lady's Hand.* 150-500 mm; common; Oct.-Apr.; flowers slightly scented.

◆ 6. **Vicia benghalensis** (= V. atropurpurea). FABACEAE (= LEGUMINOSAE). Hairy; climbing; common on roadsides and in waste places; Sept.-Nov.; introduced from Europe.

7. **Pteronia hirsuta.** ASTERACEAE (= COMPOSITAE). Small shrublet; up to 300 mm; occasional on rather dry slopes; Oct.-Dec.

8. **Senecio arenarius.** ASTERACEAE (= COMPOSITAE). *Hongerblom.* Sticky annual; frequent in sandy places; Aug.-Oct.; shade form. (See also p. 132).

9. **Roella ciliata.** CAMPANULACEAE. Scrambling or erect shrublet; up to 500 mm; frequent; mostly Oct.-Mar.

Scale: life size

1. **Aspalathus aspalathoides** (= A. anthylloides). FABACEAE
   (= LEGUMINOSAE). Shrublet; up to 200 mm; rather rare in sand on hills
   and mountains; Sept.-Nov.

2. **Indigofera glomerata.** FABACEAE (= LEGUMINOSAE). Scrambling up to
   300 mm; rather frequent on dry hill and mountain slopes; Aug.-Nov.

3. **Aspalathus capensis** (= A. sarcodes). FABACEAE (= LEGUMINOSAE).
   Dense shrub; 1 m or more; frequent on hill and mountain slopes; Aug.-
   Jan.

4. **Erica spumosa.** ERICACEAE. *Swartbekkie.* 150-500 mm; occasional on
   mountain slopes; Aug.-Nov.

5. **Erica palliiflora.** ERICACEAE. 150-500 mm; occasional in flat peaty
   places on hills; Aug.-Dec. (For white-flowered form see p. 194).

6. **Agathelpis dubia** (= A. angustifolia). SELAGINACEAE. Shrublet;
   300-500 mm; common; May-Dec.; variable in the colour of the flowers.

7. **Bolusafra bituminosa** (= Fagelia bituminosa). FABACEAE
   (= LEGUMINOSAE). Scrambling or climbing up to 1 m; common on hill
   and mountain slopes; mostly Aug.-Jan; plant tar-scented; the mountain
   form has smaller flowers.

8. **Erica pyxidiflora.** ERICACEAE. Widely branched; 300-600 mm;
   occasional over 270 m; May-Dec.

9. **Oedera imbricata** (= Eroeda imbricata). ASTERACEAE (= COMPOSITAE).
   Low shrublet; occasional on mountain slopes; Aug.-Oct.

10. **Sebaea aurea.** GENTIANACEAE. Annual; up to 200 mm; common;
    Oct.-Dec.

11. **Lotonis involucrata** subsp. **peduncularis** (= L. peduncularis).
    FABACEAE (= LEGUMINOSAE). Low creeping; frequent; Aug.-Nov. (See
    also p. 124).

12. **Satyrium bicorne.** ORCHIDACEAE. 300-500 mm; frequent in heathy
    places; Sept.-Nov.

Scale: life size

1. **Pelargonium elongatum** (= P. tabulare). GERANIACEAE. 150-300 mm; common on hill slopes, often in shade; July-Nov.; a form occurring on the southern flats has larger flowers.

2. **Wahlenbergia obovata.** CAMPANULACEAE. Annual; up to 800 mm; locally frequent on sheltered slopes in the north; Oct.-Jan.; easily confused with *W. cernua* (p. 184) in which the stigma lobes are as wide as long.

3. **Otholobium decumbens** (= Psoralea decumbens). FABACEAE (= LEGUMINOSAE). Low, matted; common; Sept.-Nov.

4. **Aspalathus cephalotes** subsp. **violacea** (= A. spicata). FABACEAE (= LEGUMINOSAE). Shrublet; 300-600 mm; frequent on hill slopes in the northern areas; Oct.-Dec.

5. **Felicia fruticosa** (= Diplopappus fruticosus). ASTERACEAE (= COMPOSITAE). *Wild Aster.* Shrub; up to 800 mm; frequent on dry slopes; Sept.-Nov.

6. **Otholobium hirtum** (= Psoralea hirta). FABACEAE (= LEGUMINOSAE). Shrub; 300 mm-1,2 m; locally plentiful on the lower slopes; Oct.-Nov.

7. **Otholobium fruticans** (= Psoralea fruticans). FABACEAE (= LEGUMINOSAE). Shrublet; up to 1 m; frequent on flats, dunes and lower slopes; Oct.-Dec.; except when growing on sand dunes it is usually dwarfed.

8. **Printzia polifolia.** ASTERACEAE (= COMPOSITAE). Low shrublet; occasional on dry western slopes in the north; Aug.-Nov.

9. **Micranthus alopecuroides** (= M. plantagineus). IRIDACEAE. 150-500 mm; frequent in sandy places; Oct.-Jan.; *M. junceus*, which grows on Rondebosh Common, has pale blue flowers and *M. tubulosus*, which is common on Lion's Head, has hollow leaves.

Scale: life size

1. **Wiborgia obcordata.** FABACEAE (= LEGUMINOSAE). Shrub; 1-1,5 m; occasional on flats; Aug.-Dec.

2. **Berkheya barbata** (= B. ilicifolia). ASTERACEAE. (= COMPOSITAE). Frequent on hill slopes; usually Sept.-Jan.

3. **Hydnora africana.** HYDNORACEAE. *Jakkalskos, Bobbejaankos, Kannip.* Very local, in sand dunes, at Llandudno; June-Jan.; parasitic on *Euphorbia caput-medusae*; flowers have an unpleasant odour.

4. **Tenicroa exuviata** (= Urginea exuviata). HYACINTHACEAE (= LILIACEAE). 300-500 mm; rare among rocks on Signal Hill and the west side of Table Mountain; Sept.-Oct.; rarely found in flower except after fires.

5. **Gazania pectinata** (= G. pinnata). ASTERACEAE (= COMPOSITAE). *Botterblom.* Frequent at low altitudes; Aug.-Nov. (See p. 144).

6. **Cyclopia genistoides.** FABACEAE (= LEGUMINOSAE). *Heuningtee.* Shrublet; 300-800 mm; frequent on hill and mountain slopes usually July-Dec. (See also p. 52).

7. **Acrolophia lamellata** (= A. capensis var. lamellata). ORCHIDACEAE. 300-600 mm; occasional on flats and mountains in the south; Oct.-Dec.

Scale: two thirds life size

1   2   3   4

5   6   7

1. **Pterygodium caffrum.** ORCHIDACEAE. 150-500 mm; occasional in damp places on hill and mountain slopes; Oct.-Dec.

2. **Ficinia radiata** (Sickmannia radiata). CYPERACEAE. *Stergras.* Occasional in sandy places, principally in the south; Sept.-Nov.

3. **Drosera hilaris.** DROSERACEAE. 150-500 mm; occasional on mountain slopes; Sept-Nov.

4. **Corycium orobanchoides.** ORCHIDACEAE. 100-300 mm; frequent in sandy places; Aug.-Oct.

5. **Satyrium coriifolium.** ORCHIDACEAE. *Ewwatrewwa, Ouma-trewwa.* 150-500 mm; occasional on flats and low mountain slopes (formerly common); July-Oct.

6. **Tritoniopsis antholyza** (= Anapalina nervosa). IRIDACEAE. 300-500 mm; frequent in stony and sandy ground on mountain slopes and plateaux; Oct.-Jan.

7. **Satyrium candidum.** ORCHIDACEAE. 150-500 mm; occasional on plateaux from Table Mountain to Muizenberg Mountain; Oct.

Scale: one-third life size

1. **Hyobanche sanguinea.** SCROPHULARIACEAE. *Katnael, Wolwekos, Skilpadblom, Soetkop.* Fleshy parasite; 100-150 mm; occasional; July-Oct.

2. **Gladiolus carneus** (= G. blandus). IRIDACEAE. *Bergpypie.* 300-500 mm; fairly frequent on mountain slopes and hills; Sept.-Nov. (See also p. 192).

3. **Disa cornuta.** ORCHIDACEAE. 300-500 mm; fairly frequent in sandy places; Oct.-Jan.

4. **Trachyandra hirsutiflora** (= Anthericum hirsutiflorum). ASPHODELACEAE (= LILIACEAE). 150-300 mm; occasional in sand, especially in the south; Aug.-Oct.

5. **Selagio spuria.** SELAGINACEAE. Annual or perennial; 150-600 mm; common; Oct.-Jan.; there is also a white form on Kenilworth Race Course.

Scale: one-third life size

Sandy Places near the Sea

1. Exomis microphylla var. **axyroides.** CHENOPODIACEAE. *Hondebossie.*
Shrublet variable in size; frequent; Nov.-Apr.

2. Senecio maritimus. ASTERACEAE (= COMPOSITAE). Sprawling annual;
frequent near the sea shore; Sept.-Mar.

3. Bulbine asphodeloides. ASPHODELACEAE (= LILIACEAE). *Wilde-kopiva,*
Geel Katstert. 150-500 mm; common in sandy places; Aug.-Nov.

4. Lightfootia tenella. CAMPANULACEAE. Shrublet; up to 500 mm;
frequent in sandy places; Oct.-Jan.

5. Monopsis lutea (= Parastranthus luteus). LOBELIACEAE (CAMPANU-
LACEAE). 150-500 mm; marsh form; occasional; Nov.-Mar. (See also
p. 70).

6. Albuca fragrans. HYACINTHACEAE (= LILIACEAE). 500-800 mm; fairly
common in the south and on Kalk Bay Mountain; Nov.-Dec.

7. Lightfootia longifolia. CAMPANULACEAE. Shrublet; up to 500 mm;
common in sandy peat, especially in the south; Nov.-Feb. (See also
p. 194).

8. Sarcocornia littorea (= Arthrocnemum littoreum). CHENOPODIACEAE.
Erect shrublet; 300-600 mm; occasional on rocks on the east coast just
above high tide mark, frequent below Paulsberg; Sept.-Dec.

9. Sonderina hispida. APIACEAE (= UMBELLIFERAE). Annual; straggling;
up to 300 mm; frequent in sand; Sept.-Nov.

10. Crassula nudicalis var. **nudicalis.** CRASSULACEAE. Stems perennial; up
to 300 mm; frequent in sandy places; Nov.-Feb.

Scale: two-thirds life size

1. **Gerbera crocea.** ASTERACEAE (= COMPOSITAE). Frequent at low altitudes; Oct.-Mar. (See also p. 158).

2. **Ixia monadelpha.** IRIDACEAE. 150-300 mm; occasional on flats and lower mountain slopes, Devil's Peak to Hout Bay; Oct.-Dec.

3. **Nemesia versicolor.** SCORPHULARIACEAE. *Weeskindertjies.* Erect annual; up to 500 mm; common; Aug.-Nov.; very variable in colour. (See also p. 156, p. 164).

4. **Ixia paniculata.** IRIDACEAE. 300-800 mm; occasional in damp places on flats and lower plateax, Kenilworth Race Course; Nov.-Dec.

5. **Athanasia dentata.** ASTERACEAE (= COMPOSITAE). Shrublet; up to 600 mm; frequent in dry places; Nov.-May.

6. **Moraea fugax** (= M. edulis). IRIDACEAE. *Uintjie.* 150-800 mm; frequent on flats and mountain slopes; Sept.-Nov. (See also p. 156 for yellow form).

7. **Senecio halimifolius.** ASTERACEAE (= COMPOSITAE). *Tabakbos.* Shrub up to 1 m; locally frequent in damp places on flats; Nov.-Jan.; sometimes used for wind breaks.

● 8. **Harveya squamosa.** SCROPHULARIACEAE. Parasitic herb; up to 500 mm; rather rare near the coast from Smitswinkel to the south; Oct.-Dec.

Scale: two-thirds life size

1. **Disa draconis.** ORCHIDACEAE. 250-500 mm; local, between Grassy Park and Zeekoevlei and near Princess Vlei, also on Table back near Woodhead reservoir; Nov.-Dec.; leaves wither as the flowers develop.

2. **Rhynchosia ferulifolia.** FABACEAE (= LEGUMINOSAE). Prostrate; occasional on sand flats – Retreat, Hout Bay and Chapman's Bay; Sept.-Jan.; *R. pinnata*, occurring at Witsand and Chapman's Bay, closely resembles this, but has pinnate leaves.

3. **Heliophila linearis** var. **linaerifolia** (= H. elongata). BRASSICACEAE (= CRUCIFERAE). Straggling perennial; frequent on lower slopes; Dec.-Mar.; variable in colour.

4. **Othonna coronopifolia.** ASTERACEAE (= COMPOSITAE). Shrub; up to 1 m; frequent in sandy places at low altitudes; May-Feb.

● 5. **Serruria foeniculacea.** PROTEACEAE. 300-500 mm; rare on flats, near Zeekoevlei and Raapenberg; Oct.-Nov.

6. **Aspalathus ternata.** FABACEAE (= LEGUMINOSAE). Shrublet; 500-800 mm; rather rare on sandy flats – Retreat, Ysterplaat, Milnerton; Oct.-Dec. Current status unknown.

Scale: life size

1

2

3

4

5

6

1. **Watsonia tabularis** (= W. tabularis var. concolor). IRIDACEAE. About 900 mm-1,7 m; frequent on marshy places from Red Hill to Cape Point, occasional on mountains from Constantiaberg to Kalk Bay; Nov.-Feb.; the typical form on Table Mountain has salmon-coloured flowers.

2. **Ornithogalum thyrsoides.** HYACINTHACEAE (LILIACEAE). *Chinkerinchee, Tjienkerientjee.* 200-600 mm; common; Oct.-Dec.

3. **Senecio rigidus.** ASTERACEAE (= COMPOSITAE). Shrub; up to 2,5 m; frequent in sheltered places; Dec- Jan.

4. **Leucospermum conocarpodendron** (= L. conocarpum). PROTEACEAE. *Pincushion, Kreupelhout, Goudblom.* Shrub; up to 3 m; common on lower slopes; Aug.-Jan.

5. **Bonatea speciosa.** ORCHIDACEAE. 300-600 mm; rare, in shade at Buffels Bay and Hout Bay; Oct.-Nov.

Scale: one-third life size

1

2

3

4

5

1. **Wahlenbergia cernua.** CAMPANULACEAE. Annual; up to 300 mm; occasional (intermittent); Nov.-Dec.; differs from *W. obovata* (p. 168) in that the lobes of the stigma are as wide as long.

2. **Thereianthus bracteolatus.** IRIDACEAE. 150-300 mm; occasional in sandy ground on mountain slopes and plateaux; Nov.-Jan.

3. **Lightfootia subulata** (L. fruticosa). CAMPANULACEAE. Sprawling; frequent on low slopes; Nov.-Mar.

4. **Ornithogalum hispidum** subsp. **bergii.** HYACINTHACEAE (= LILIACEAE). 150-500 mm; common lower slopes and sandy flats; Nov.-Feb.

◆ 5. **Lythrum hyssopifolia.** LYTHRACEAE. Annual; 150-200 mm; frequent on damp flats; Nov.-Jan.; native to Europe.

6. **Falkia repens.** CONVOLVULACEAE. Prostrate; occasional on flats and near vleis; Nov.- Dec.

7. **Laurentia secunda.** CAMPANULACEAE. Annual; frequent in damp places; Nov.-Mar.

8. **Oxalis incarnata.** OXALIDACEAE. Common in forests and shady places; Aug.-Dec., also Mar.-Apr.; stems branching.

9. **Pelargonium myrrhifolium** var. **myrrhifolium.** GERANIACEAE. 150-300 mm; very common on flats and mountains; May-Feb.; very variable in the size of the flowers and lobing of the leaves. (See also p. 86).

◆ 10. **Convolvulus arvenis.** CONVOLVULACEAE. *Bindweed.* Climbing or prostrate; occasional, on roadsides and cultivated land; Nov.-Jan.; introduced from Europe.

11. **Ixia scillaris** (= Tritonia scillaris). IRIDACEAE. 200-400 mm; occasional on lower slopes from Cape Town to Hout Bay; Sept.-Nov., especially after fires.

Scale: life size

1. **Lobostemon argenteus.** BORAGINACEAE. Shrub; up to 1 m; occasional on dry slopes; Nov.-Jan.

2. **Aristea macrocarpa.** IRIDACEAE. 460 mm – 1,4 m; frequent on mountains and flats, occasional on flats from Kenilworth to Retreat; Nov.-Dec.

3. **Scabiosa africana.** DIPSACACEAE. *Scabious.* Up to 1 m; frequent on sheltered slopes; July-Nov.

4. **Carpobrotus edulis.** MESEMBRYANTHEMACEAE. *Sour Fig, Perdevy.* Robust, creeping perennial; common in sand near the sea, frequent on flats and slopes; Aug.-Nov.; pale yellow, becoming pink with age.

5. **Rafnia triflora.** FABACEAE (= LEGUMINOSAE). Shrub; 1-2 m; occasional on hill slopes; Sept.-Jan.

6. **Ursinea paleacea** (= U. crithmoides). ASTERACEAE (= COMPOSITAE). Shrublet; up to 800 mm; frequent; July-Apr.

7. **Ixia polystachya.** IRIDACEAE. 300-800 mm; frequent in damp or shade on flats and mountain slopes, locally common above Kirstenbosch; Oct.-Dec.

8. **Berkheya armata.** ASTERACEAE (= COMPOSITAE). 150-500 mm; common on hill slopes; Aug.-Jan.

9. **Dilatris pillansii.** HAEMODORACEAE (= TECOPHILAEACEAE). *Rooiwortel.* 300-500 mm; frequent on slopes and plateaux and on the southern flats; Aug.-Jan.; differs from the very similar *D. corymbosa* in having all the stamens shorter than the perianth.

Scale: one-third life size

1. **Crassula pruinosa** x **C. scabra.** CRASSULACEAE. Slightly woody perennial; 150-300 mm; occasional on rocks on lower slopes; Nov.- Feb.

2. **Euphorbia arceuthobioides.** EUPHORBIACEAE. Succulent shrublet; up to 300 mm; confined to the saddle and rump on the west slopes of Lion's Head; Sept.-Nov.; male and female flowers occur on separate plants, female illustrated.

3. **Agathosma ciliata.** RUTACEAE. *Steenbok buchu.* Up to 600 mm; occasional, usually in thick bush on sandy slopes above 166 m; mostly Apr.-Sept.

4. **Ornithogalum suaveolens** (= O. barbatum). HYACINTHACEAE (= LILIACEAE). 150-300 mm; locally common on the lower slopes of Lion's Head and near Kommetjie; Nov.

5. **Linum africanum.** LINACEAE. *Flax.* Erect or straggling; frequent on the lower slopes; mostly Oct.-Dec.

6. **Euryops pectinatus.** ASTERACEAE (= COMPOSITAE). Shrub; up to 1 m; occasional in rocky places in mountains; Oct.-Dec.

7. **Salvia chamelaeagnea.** LAMIACEAE (= LABIATAE). Shrublet; 600-900 mm; frequent on hill slopes; Nov.-Apr.; calyx does not enlarge in fruiting stage as it does in *S. africana-caerulea* (p.88).

8. **Tetragonia fruticosa.** AIZOACEAE. *Kinkelklappers, Kinkelbossie.* Common in sand; very variable species; Sept.-Nov.

Scale: life size

1. **Herschelianthe purpurascens** (= Herschelia purpurascens). ORCHIDACEAE. 300-500 mm; fairly frequent in heathy places in the south; Oct.-Nov.; scented like stewed blackberries.

2. **Lobelia coronopifolia.** LOBELIACEAE (= CAMPANULACEAE). 150-500 mm; common on low slopes; Nov.-Mar.

3. **Lobelia comosa.** LOBELIACEAE (= CAMPANULACEAE). Up to 500 mm; frequent; Nov.-May.

4. **Psoralea aphylla.** FABACEAE·(= LEGUMINOSAE). *Bloukeur, Fonteinbos.* Shrub; 1-1,5 m; frequent in marshy places and by streamsides; Oct.-Jan.

5. **Aspalathus callosa.** FABACEAE (= LEGUMINOSAE). Erect shrublet; 300-500 mm; common on flats; Nov.-Dec.

6. **Gnidia oppositifolia.** THYMELAEAECEAE. Erect shrub; up to 2 m; frequent by streamsides and in marshes; mostly Oct.-Jan.

7. **Linum thunbergii.** LINACEAE. *Flax.* Erect; up to 500 mm; occasional in damp places, especially in the south; Oct.-Jan.

8. **Aristea juncifolia.** IRIDACEAE. 300-500 mm. Occasional near marshes in the south; Nov.-Dec.

9. **Lobelia pinifolia.** LOBELIACEAE (= CAMPANULACEAE). Shrublet; 300-600 mm; common on slopes; mainly Sept.-Dec., but almost throughout the year.

10. **Aristea africana.** IRIDACEAE. 100-300 mm; common on flats, mountain slopes and plateaux; Aug.-Dec.

11. **Gnidia penicillata.** THYMELAEAECEAE. Shrublet; 150-300 mm; occasional in marshy places in the south; Oct.-May; small-flowered form; the large-flowered form does not occur in the Cape Peninsula.

12. **Psoralea pinnata.** FABACEAE (= LEGUMINOSAE). *Bloukeur.* Shrub; 1,5 m-3 m; common; Oct.-Dec.

13. **Disa tenuifolia** (= D. patens). ORCHIDACEAE. 50-150 mm; frequent in damp peaty soil on mountains and southern flats; Nov-Dec.

Scale: life size

1. **Gladiolus carneus** (= G. macowanianus). IRIDACEAE. *Painted Lady.* Southern form; 300-500 mm; frequent in marshy places from Constantiaberg to the south; Oct.-Jan. (See also p. 174).

2. **Lampranthus emarginatus.** MESEMBRYANTHEMACEAE. Erect; 100-300 mm; common in clay or sand; Nov.-Feb.; very variable. (See also p. 48).

3. **Diastella divaricata** (= D. serpyllifolia). PROTEACEAE. Scrambling shrublet; up to 500 mm; common on flats and hills, especially in the south; Jan.-Dec.; a rare prostrate form occurs near Smith's Farm.

4. **Staavia radiata.** BRUNIACEAE. *Altydbos.* Dense shrublet; 600-800 mm; common at most altitudes; Jan.-Dec.

5. **Chironia baccifera.** GENTIANACEAE. *Christmas Berry, Aambeibossie.* Dense shrublet up to 500 mm; frequent; Nov.-Feb.; berries red.

6. **Cryptadenia grandiflora.** THYMELAEAECEAE. Shrublet; about 300 mm; frequent, especially in the south; usually Sept.-Nov. (See also p. 92).

7. **Roella amplexicaulis.** CAMPANULACEAE. Erect; 300-500 mm; frequent among rocks in the south; Nov.-Mar.; usually with several flowers in a head.

8. **Erica pulchella.** ERICACEAE. Up to 300 mm; common, especially in the south; Aug.-Dec.

9. **Erica obliqua.** ERICACEAE. 300-500 mm; occasional in peaty flats, especially in the south; Nov.-Mar.

10. **Chironia decumbens.** GENTIANACEAE. Creeping or erect; up to 300 mm; frequent in marshy places at low altitudes; Nov.-June.

11. **Orphium frutescens.** GENTIANACEAE. Erect; 500-600 mm; frequent in sandy places, often near the sea; Nov.-Feb.

12. **Chironia linoides** subsp. **emarginata** (= C. emarginata). GENTIANACEAE. Erect; 100-200 mm; frequent; Nov.-Jan.

13. **Erica hirtiflora.** ERICACEAE. Up to 800 mm; common on mountain slopes and in marshes; Nov.-Apr.; later at higher altitudes. (See also p. 46).

14. **Erica corifolia.** ERICACEAE. 300-500 mm; common; Oct.-May; size of flowers very variable.

Scale: life size

● **1. Gladiolus vigilans.** IRIDACEAE. 300-600 mm; very local, in dry ground on Vasco da Gama Peak; Nov.

2. Erica bruniades. ERICACEAE. *Kapokkie.* 300-500 mm; southern form; common in marshes and damp peaty flats; July-Jan.; in the more northerly form the flowers are much more hairy, with white hairs.

3. Pelargonium longifolium. GERANIACEAE. Tuberous; 100-200 mm; frequent; Nov.-Jan.; very variable – the leaf blades may be all lance-shaped, all deeply and narrowly cut, or both on the same plant. (See also p. 210).

4. Struthiola ciliata. THYMELAEAECEAE. Shrublet; 300 mm-1,2 m; very common; Jan.-Dec.; tube of the flower hairy; flowers more often white.

5. Corymbium africanum. ASTERACEAE (= COMPOSITAE). Up to 300 mm; frequent, especially after fires; Oct.-Jan.

6. Lightfootia longifolia. CAMPANULACEAE. Shrublet; up to 500 mm; common in sandy peat, especially in the south; Nov.-Feb. (See also p. 176).

7. Brachycarpaea juncea (= B. laxa). BRASSICACEAE (= CRUCIFERAE). Trailing or erect; local, near Vasco da Gama Peak and above Smith's Farm; Sept.-Nov.

8. Senecio umbellatus. ASTERACEAE (= COMPOSITAE). Up to 800 mm; occasional on lower slopes; Oct.-Dec.

9. Lachnaea densiflora. THYMELAEAECEAE. Shrublet; about 200 mm; occasional, more frequent in the south; Aug.-Dec.

10. Erica palliiflora. ERICACEAE. 150-500 mm; occasional in flat peaty places on hills; Aug.-Dec. (For the pink form see p. 166).

11. Passerina vulgaris. THYMELAEAECEAE. *Gonnabos.* Shrub; 1-3,5 m; very common; Oct.-Nov.; flowers vary from yellow to dull red.

12. Aspalathus tridentata. FABACEAE (= LEGUMINOSAE). Shrublet; up to 300 mm; occasional on flats and hills; Sept.-Jan.

Scale: life size

1. **Ixia dubia.** IRIDACEAE. *Yellow Ixia, Geelkalossie.* 300-600 mm; frequent on open spaces on western mountain slopes, common on Kenilworth Race Course; Oct.-Dec.

2. **Aspalathus ericifolia.** FABACEAE (= LEGUMINOSAE). Shrublet; 300- 600 mm; common on hill slopes; Sept.-Nov.

3. **Aspalathus ciliaris.** FABACEAE (= LEGUMINOSAE). Shrublet; up to 600 mm; frequent on flats and hill slopes; Nov.-Jan.; very variable in habit, sometimes with the inflorescence elongated.

4. **Aspalathus divaricata.** FABACEAE (= LEGUMINOSAE). Shrublet; 300-500 mm; frequent on hillsides; Sept.-Mar.; very variable in habit and the number of flowers.

5. **Edmondia sesamoides** (= Helichrysum sesamoides). ASTERACEAE (= COMPOSITAE). Shrublet; 300-500 mm; common; Aug.-Dec.; flowers everlasting.

6. **Moraea neglecta.** IRIDACEAE. 300-600 mm; frequent on peat or sandy flats, mountain slopes and plateaux; Aug.-Nov.; rather a deeper yellow than *M. angusta.* (See p. 146).

7. **Hexaglottis virgata.** IRIDACEAE. 300-600 mm; frequent on dry lower slopes from Signal Hill to Muizenberg; Oct.-Dec.; differs from *H. flexuosa* in having concealed fruits and the flowers pressed against the stem.

8. **Chrysocoma coma-aurea.** ASTERACEAE (= COMPOSITAE). Shrublet; up to 500 mm; frequent; Sept.-Nov. (See also p. 92).

9. **Osteospermum polygaloides.** ASTERACEAE (= COMPOSITAE). Low shrublet; rarely over 500 mm high; frequent at low altitudes; mainly Aug.-Jan.

10. **Gnidia juniperifolia.** THYMELAEAECEAE. Dense shrublet; 150-500 mm; frequent on lower slopes; Jan.-Dec.; variable in size of flowers; a small-flowered form occurs on Wynberg Hill.

11. **Athanasia crithmifolia.** ASTERACEAE (= COMPOSITAE). Shrublet; up to 800 mm; frequent in the south; Oct.-Dec.

12. **Monadenia densiflora** (= M. auriculata). ORCHIDACEAE. 150-300 mm; occasional in marshes on mountains and the southern flats; Oct.-Nov.

Scale: life size

1. **Felicia aethiopica.** ASTERACEAE (= COMPOSITAE). Straggling shrublet; frequent in bushy places on slopes; Jan.-Dec.

2. **Moraea tripetala.** IRIDACEAE. 200-400 mm; frequent on upper mountain slopes; Oct.-Dec. (See also p. 114).

3. **Pelargonium tabulare.** (= P. saniculaefolium). GERANIACEAE. 300-500 mm; frequent on hillsides in the northern areas; Nov.-Dec.

● 4. **Erica marifolia.** ERICACEAE. Spreading dwarf; rather rare, in crevices and caves in the mountains; Nov.-Apr.

5. **Erica glutinosa.** ERICACEAE. 150-300 mm; frequent on mountains in the northern areas; Nov.-May; very sticky.

6. **Erica multumbellifera.** ERICACEAE. Much-branched; 150-500 mm; common on flats, hills and plateaux; Nov.-May.

7. **Harveya purpurea.** SCROPHULARIACEAE. Parasitic herb; up to 300 mm; frequent, chiefly south of Constantiaberg; Nov.-Dec.

8. **Indigofera filiformis.** FABACEAE (= LEGUMINOSAE). Scrambling or erect; 300-600 mm; frequent on hill slopes in the northern areas; July-Dec.

9. **Silene undulata** (= Melandrium undulatum). CARYOPHYLLACEAE. Spreading stems 400-800 mm long; frequent in shady places; Sept.-Nov.; flowers occasionally deep red. (See also p. 150).

10. **Helichrysum spiralepis** (= Leontonyx squarrosus). ASTERACEAE (= COMPOSITAE). Up to 300 mm; occasional in the north; Nov.-Feb.

11. **Helichrysum patulum** (= H. crispum). ASTERACEAE (= COMPOSITAE). *Hottentot Bedding, Hottentotskooigoed.* Straggling, much-branched; frequent on hill slopes; Nov.-Jan.

12. **Psoralea aculeata.** FABACEAE (= LEGUMINOSAE). Aromatic shrub; up to 1 m; frequent on slopes in the northern areas; Aug.-Nov.

Scale: life size

Orchidaceae

1. **Disa racemosa.** 300-600 mm; occasional in marshes; Nov.-Jan.

2. **Disa atricapilla** (= Orthopenthea atricapilla). 100-300 mm; occasional in marshy places in the south; Nov.-Dec.

3. **Pterygodium acutifolium.** 150-300 mm; locally common in marshy places; Nov.-Dec.; soap-like scent.

● 4. **Acrolophia bolusii.** 300-600 mm; occasional in sandy places, chiefly in the south; Nov.-Dec.

5. **Ceratandra atrata.** 150-300 mm; frequent in marshes on mountains and on southern flats; Nov.-Dec.

6. **Monadenia reticulata.** 150-300 mm; occasional in sand on mountains – Steenberg and Table Mountain near Grootkop; Nov.-Dec.

Scale: two-third life size

1. **Villarsia capensis.** (= V. ovata). GENTIANACEAE. Up to 500 mm; frequent in marshes; Oct.-Feb.

2. **Samolus porosus.** PRIMULACEAE. Erect; up to 500 mm; locally frequent in marshes; Nov.-Feb.

3. **Watsonia borbonica** (= W. pyramidata). IRIDACEAE. *Suurkanol, Suurknol.* 800 mm-1,5 m; common on mountain slopes and hills; Oct.-Nov.

Scale: two-third life size

1. Moraea viscaria (= M. odorata). IRIDACEAE. 300-500 mm; occasional on sandy flats – Rondebosch Common, Milnerton and Grassy Park; Nov.-Dec.; flowers open mid-afternoon; stem sticky; sweet-scented.

2. Syncarpha vestita (= Helichrysum vestitum). ASTERACEAE (= COMPOSITAE). *Everlasting, Sewejaartjie.* Compact shrub up to 800 mm; common, especially in the south; Nov.-Jan.

3. Lapeirousia anceps (= L. fabricii). IRIDACEAE. 150-300 mm; frequent on sandy flats; Nov.-Dec.

4. Heliophila digitata (= H. integrifolia var. digitata). BRASSICACEAE (= CRUCIFERAE). Annual; up to 900 mm; common in sandy soil; Aug.-Dec. (See also p. 140).

5. Salvia lanceolata (= S. nivea). LAMIACEAE (= LABIATAE). Shrub; 800 mm-1 m; occasional on sandy flats; Nov.-Feb.

6. Aspalathus laricifolia ssp. **laricifolia.** FABACEAE (= LEGUMINOSAE). Low shrublet; occasional on dry hill slopes; Sept.-Dec.; another form of this with grey leaves is sometimes distinguished as *A. laricifolia* ssp. *canescens.*

Scale: two-third life size

1. Aspalathus angustifolia (= Borbonia lanceolata). FABACEAE (= LEGUMINOSAE). Shrublet; 300-600 mm; frequent on flats; Nov.-Mar.

2. Gladiolus undulatus (= G. cuspidatus). IRIDACEAE. 600-900 mm; rare, by the Silvermine and on Steenberg Plateau, but rarely flowering; Nov.-Dec.; occasional at low altitudes.

3. Prismatocarpus fruticosus. (= P. subulatus). CAMPANULACEAE. Straggling shrublet; 500-800 mm; frequent on dry slopes; Dec-Apr.; flowers white when fresh.

4. Herschelianthe hians (= Herschelia hians). ORCHIDACEAE. 300-500 mm; rare on flats at Kenilworth Race Course, possibly extinct on Peninsula; Sept.-Dec.

5. Aspalathus sericea (= A. linifolius). FABACEAE (= LEGUMINOSAE). Erect shrublet; 300-500 mm; frequent on flats and hill plateaux; Sept.-Jan.

6. Othonna dentata. ASTERACEAE (= COMPOSITAE). Low succulent shrub; occasional among rocks on mountains; May-Dec.

7. Lotononis fastigiata (= L. angustifolia). FABACEAE (= LEGUMINOSAE). Erect; 150-300 mm; rare, on sandy flats and hills, Steenberg Plateau; Dec.-Feb.

8. Gethyllis afra. AMARYLLIDACEAE. *Kukumakranka, Koekoemakranka.* Locally common on Rondebosch Common; Dec.; leaves narrow, spirally twisted.

Scale: two-third life size

1. **Aspalathus araneosa.** FABACEAE (= LEGUMINOSAE). Straggling shrublet; up to 500 mm; occasional on eastern slopes from Newlands to Fish Hoek; Oct.-Dec.

2. **Aspalathus astroites.** FABACEAE (= LEGUMINOSAE). Dense, prickly shrub; 1 m or more; common on slopes in the northern areas; Sept.-Dec.; rather like *Gorse.*

3. **Aspalathus juniperina** (= A. galioides). FABACEAE (= LEGUMINOSAE). Procumbent; branching stems 300-600 mm long; occasional on hill slopes, especially in the south; Oct.-Jan.

4. **Aspalathus spinosa.** FABACEAE (= LEGUMINOSAE). Prickly shrublet; 500 mm-1 m; common; Nov.-Apr.

5. **Aspalathus cordata** (= Borbonia cordata). FABACEAE (= LEGUMINOSAE). Prickly shrub; 500 mm-1 m; common; Sept.-Dec.

◆ 6. **Cytisus candicans** (= C. monspessulanus). FABACEAE (= LEGUMINOSAE). Shrub; 1-2 m; rather local in forests – Newlands Avenue, Klein Constantia and Orange Kloof; Sept.-Dec.; introduced from southern Europe.

7. **Athanasia trifurcata.** ASTERACEAE (= COMPOSITAE). *Klaas Louwbossie, Kouterbossie.* Shrublet; up to 600 mm; frequent on dry slopes, especially in the north; Nov.-Mar.

8. **Pelargonium rapaceum.** GERANIACEAE. *Bergaartappel.* Tuberous; 100-200 mm; frequent on Signal Hill, occasional on flats; Nov.-Dec.; pink forms also occur.

9. **Moraea bituminosa.** IRIDACEAE. *Teeruintjie.* 300-500 mm; frequent on flats and lower mountain slopes; Oct.-Dec.; stem sticky.

10. **Aspalathus cymbiformis** (= A. uniflora). FABACEAE (= LEGUMINOSAE). Scrambling shrublet; 300-500 mm; frequent on hillsides; Oct.-Mar.

11. **Hibiscus aethiopicus.** MALVACEAE. Dwarf; stems procumbent, 50-300 mm long; common; Apr.-Jan., especially after fires.

Scale: life size

1. **Polygala garcini.** POLYGALACEAE. Erect; up to 500 mm; frequent; Sept.-Jan.

2. **Monopsis simplex** (= M. debilis). CAMPANULACEAE. Annual; up to 150 mm; frequent in wet places; Sept.-Feb. (See also p. 138).

3. **Centella tridentata.** APIACEAE (= UMBELLIFERAE). Up to 200 mm; frequent on hills; Sept.-Dec.

4. **Lachnaea capitata.** THYMELAEAECEAE. Shrublet; up to 500 mm; occasional as far south as Fish Hoek, Kenilworth Race Course; July-Jan.

5. **Muraltia.** Species unidentifiable. POLYGALACEAE. Kommetjie.

6. **Aizoon paniculatum.** AIZOACEAE. 80-300 mm; occasional on sandy flats; Sept.-Dec.

7. **Pelargonium longifolium.** GERANIACEAE. Tuberous; 100-200 mm; frequent on flats and hillsides; Nov.-Jan.; leaves very variable. (See also p. 194).

● 8. **Erica capitata.** ERICACEAE. About 300 mm; occasional on flats at Kenilworth, Kommetjie, Witsand; Oct.-Feb.

Scale: life size

1   2   3   4   5

6   7   8

Mountain Plants

● **1. Staavia glutinosa.** BRUNIACEAE. Shrublet; up to 800 mm; occasional on the upper parts of Table Mountain and Muizenberg Mountain; irregular in flowering.

2. Erica mollis. ERICACEAE. 300-500 mm; occasional on mountains, especially Table Mountain; Nov.-Feb.

3. Disperis paludosa. ORCHIDACEAE. 150-500 mm; occasional in marshes on mountains and on flats in the south; Nov.-Dec.

4. Felicia cymbalariae. ASTERACEAE (= COMPOSITAE). Straggling; occasional in shady places under rocks at high altitudes; Nov.-Mar.

5. Grubbia rosmarinifolia. GRUBBIACEAE. Erect shrub; 500 mm-1,4 m; frequent in marshes on mountains over 465 m; mostly Aug.-Sept.

6. Disa rosea (= Orthopenthea rosea). ORCHIDACEAE. 70-200 mm; occasional on moist shady ridges and in rock clefts on mountains; Nov.-Dec.

7. Mairea crenata. ASTERACEAE (= COMPOSITAE). Occasional in rocky crevices on mountains; Sept.-Dec.

8. Crassula pellucida subsp. **pellucida.** CRASSULACEAE. 100-500 mm; scrambling perennial; frequent in damp places, usually on mountains; Oct.-Apr.

Scale: life size

1
2
3
4
5
6
7
8

1. **Aspidoglossum heterophyllum** (= Schizoglossum heterophyllum). ASCLEPIADACEAE. 100-150 mm; occasional on low hills and mountain slopes; Sept.-Feb.

2. **Holothrix villosa** var. **condensata** (= H. condensata). ORCHIDACEAE. Up to 200 mm; occasional on wet rocks and ledges on mountains; Nov.-Dec.

3. **Disa filicornis** (= Penthea filicornis). ORCHIDACEAE. 100-200 mm; occasional in damp peaty soil – Kenilworth Race Course, Steenberg Plateau, Red Hill, Klaasjagers; Oct.-Dec.

4. **Printzia aromatica.** ASTERACEAE (= COMPOSITAE). Low shrublet; up to 300 mm; occasional on mountain slopes in the north; Nov.-Feb.; strongly aromatic.

5. **Erica tenuis.** ERICACEAE. Dwarf; usually spreading in a moss-like manner in the Peninsula; in rock crevices and on ledges on hills and mountains; Oct.-Dec.

6. **Eulophia aculeata** (= E. capensis). ORCHIDACEAE. Up to 300 mm; fairly frequent, usually in marshes, rare on flats; Nov.-Jan.

7. **Lightfootia parvifolia.** CAMPANULACEAE. Stems prostrate or straggling; 200-800 mm long; frequent among rocks; Dec.-Mar.

8. **Aspalathus crenata** (= Borbonia parviflora). FABACEAE (= LEGUMI-NOSAE). Straggling shrublet; 300-600 mm; occasional on dry slopes; Oct.-Jan.

9. **Harveya tubulosa.** SCROPHULARIACEAE. *Inkblom.* Parasitic herb; 150-500 mm; frequent; Oct.-Mar.

Scale: life size

1

2

3

4

5

6

7

8

9

1. **Satyridium rostratum.** ORCHIDACEAE. 150-500 mm; occasional in marshy places – Steenberg, Table Mountain and Muizenberg Mountain; Dec.

2. **Eulophia tabularis.** ORCHIDACEAE. 150-500 mm; occasional in marshy places on mountains; Dec.-Jan.

3. **Indigofera psoraleoides.** FABACEAE (= LEGUMINOSAE). 300-500 mm; occasional on flats and lower slopes; Sept.-Dec.; distinguished from *I. nitida*, (see p. 158), in that the hairs on the leaflets lie almost longitudinally.

4. **Cyrtanthus ventricosus.** AMARYLLIDACEAE. *Brandlelie.* 100-200 mm; locally common in the south; Dec.-May, usually after fires; leaves narrow.

5. **Erica haematocodon.** ERICACEAE. Tortuous, matted, branched dwarf; rare on cliffs and in damp crevices, over 465 m – Constantiaberg, Swartkop and Noordhoek Peak; Dec.-Jan.

6. **Erica transparens.** ERICACEAE. Up to 300 mm; occasional on mountains in the northern half of the Peninsula; Dec.-Mar.

7. **Schizodium inflexum.** ORCHIDACEAE. Up to 300 mm; occasional on the upper and lower plateaux on Table Mountain; Dec.

8. **Erica oxycoccifolia.** ERICACEAE. Dwarf, straggling, procumbent; occasional in damp rock crevices on mountains in the northern area; Dec.-Feb.

9. **Disa vaginata.** ORCHIDACEAE. Up to 150 mm; occasional in damp sandy or marshy places, often among Restionaceae; Oct.-Dec.

Scale: life size

1

2

3

4

5

6

7

8

9

Glossary

alternate: placed alternately one above the other, usually pertaining to leaf arrangement on the stem (see fig. 1)

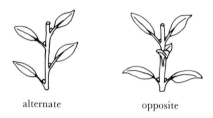

alternate   opposite

Fig. 1 Leaf arrangements

annual: a plant that completes its life cycle in one year or less
anther: upper portion of the stamen which produces the pollen (see fig. 2)

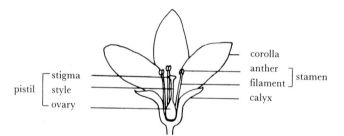

Fig. 2 A longitudinal section of a typical flower

Fig. 3 A typical leaf

axil: the angle between the branch and the leaf stalk (see fig. 3)

218

biennial: a plant that completes its life cycle in two years or less

bulb: a subterranean storage organ made up of succulent leaf bases

calyx: outer series of leaf-like segments of a flower, frequently green and enclosing the rest of the flower in bud, sometimes large and colourful, sometimes absent (see fig. 2)

corm: a subterranean storage organ which is a modified stem

corolla: the whorl of petals, usually coloured, in the flower (see fig. 2)

deciduous: the shedding of leaves at a particular time or season

evergreen: in leaf throughout the year

filament: stalk of the anther (see fig. 2)

glabrous: hairless

herb: a plant with no woody parts above ground

midrib: the principal vein in the middle of the leaf which is a continuation of the petiole (see fig. 3)

opposite: two at a node, on opposing sides of a stem (see fig. 1)

ovary: that part of the flower that contains the ovules and eventually becomes the fruit

perennial: a plant which lives for more than two years

petal: a unit of the corolla of a flower, usually coloured and more or less showy

petiole: a leaf stalk (see fig. 3)

sepal: a unit of the calyx, usually green

stamen: the male part of a flower, consisting of anthers and filament (see fig. 2)

stigma: the part of the style which receives the pollen (fig. 2)

tuber: a subterranean storage organ which is a modified root

Index to Botanical Names

Protected species are marked with an asterisk ⋆ (see Schedule 4 of ordinance 19, 1974; pp. 237-239).

In the text rare and possibly extinct species are marked with a ● and introduced species are marked with a ◆.

A

Achythanthes sicula (L.) All., 98
Acrolophia bolusii Rolfe, 200
  capensis Bergius) Fourc. var. *lamellata* (Lindley) Schelpe, 170
  lamellata (Lindl.) Schltr. & H. Bol., 170
Adenandra *umbellata* Willd. 122, 150 uniflora (L.) Willd., 80
  villosa (Bergius) Lichtenst. ex Roemer & Schultes 122, 150
Adenogramma lichtensteiniana (Ser.) Druce, 142
Adromischus hemisphaericus (L.) Lem., 76
  rotundifolius (Harvey) C.A.Smith, 76
Agapanthus africanus (L.) Hoffsgg., 34
Agathelpis *angustifolia*, 166
  dubia (L.) Hutchinson ex Wijnands, 166
Agathosma ciliaris (L.) Druce, 116
  ciliata (L.) Link, 188
  serpyllacea (Roemer & Schultes) Lichtenst., 16
Aizoon paniculatum L., 210
  sarmentosum L.f., 120
Allbuca canadensis (L.) F.M. Leighton, 134
  cooperi Baker, 160
  fragrans Jacq., 176
Alciope tabularis (Thunb.) DC., 54
Amaryllis belladonna L., 58
Amellus asteroides (L.) Druce, 132
Amphithalea ericofolia (L.) Ecklon & Zeyher, 86
  imbricata (L.) Druce, 38
Anagallis arvensis L. var. caerulea Lindley, 154
Anapalina nervosa (Thunb.) G. Lewis, 172
  triticea (Burm.f.) N.E. Br.,34
Anaxeton *asperum* (Thunb.) DC., 92
  laeve (Harvey) Lundgren, 92
Androcymbium eucomoides (Jacq.) Willd., 104
Anemone *capensis* Lam., 110
  tenuifolia (L.f.) DC., 110
Anisodontea scabrosa (L.) D. Bates, 100
Anomalesia cunonia (L.) N.E. Br., 148
Anthericum brachypodum Baker, 80
  ciliatum L.f., 114
  hirsutiflorum Adamson, 174

hispidum L., 88
revolutum L., 98
Antholyza ringens L., 122
Anthospermum *ciliare* L., 108
  galioides Reichb. f. ssp. galioides, 108
Apium inundatum (L.) Teichb.f., 112
Aponogeton angustifolius Aiton, 112
  distachyos L.f., 130
Arctopus echinatus L., 128
Arctotheca calendula (L.) Levyns, 148
Arctotis acaulis L., 116
  aspera L., 52
  hirsuta (Harvey) Lewin, 134
Aristea africana (L.) Hoffsgg., 190
  juncifolia Baker, 190
  macrocarpa G. Lewis, 186
  spiralis (L.f.) Ker Gawler, 146
Arthrocnemum littoreum Moss., 176
Asclepias cancellata Burm.f., 76
  fruticosa L., 66
  pubescens L., 76
Aspalathus angustifolia (Lam.) R. Dahlgren, 206
  anthylloides L., 166
  araneosa L., 208
  arida E. Meyer, 30
  aspalathoides (L.) R. Dahlgren, 166
  astroites L., 208
  barbata (Lam.) R. Dahlgren, 38
  callosa L., 190
  capensis (Walp.) R. Dahlgren, 166
  capitata L., 144
  carnosa Bergius, 142
  cephalotes Thunb. subsp. violacea R. Dahlgren,, 168
  ciliaris L., 196
  cordata L., 208
  crenata (L.) R. Dahlgren, 214
  cymbiformis DC., 208
  divaricata Thunb., 196
  ericifolia L., 196
  galioides Thunb., 196
  juniperina Thunb., 208
  laricifolia Bergius 204
  laricifolia Bergius ssp. laricifolia, 204
  linifolius Steudel, 206
  sarcodes (Vogel) Walp., 166

221

List of families and Genera

(only illustrated Families and genera are included).
Numbers against each genus indicate the number of species (including subspecies and varieties)
occuring in these genera in the Cape Peninsula. Numbers in brackets indicate the number of
species illustrated in this guide.

Diplopappus (see Felicia)
Disparago Gaertn., 3 **(1)**
Edmondia Cass., 2 **(1)**
Eriocephalus L., 2 **(1)**
Eroeda (see Oedera)
Euryops Cass., 2 **(2)**
Felicia Cass., 13 **(6)**
Gazania Gaertn., 2 **(1)**
Gerbera L., 5 **(2)**
Gibbaria Cass., 1
Gorteria L., 1
Gnaphalium (see
  Pseudognaphalium)
Gymnodiscus Less., 1
Haplocarpha Less., 1
Helichrysum Mill., 30 **(8)**
Ifloga Cass., 3 **(1)**
Kleinia (see Senecio)
Lasiospermum Lag., 1
Leontonix (see Helichrysum)
Leysera L., 1
Mairia Nees, 3 **(1)**
Matricaria (see Oncosiphon)
Metalasia R. Br., 3 **(2)**
Nidorella Cass., 1
Oedera L., 3 **(3)**
Oncosiphon Kallersjo 4 **(1)**
Osmitopsis Cass. emend.
  Bremer, 2 **(1)**
Osteospermum L., 9 **(4)**
Othonna L., 14 **(9)**
Petalacte D. Don 1
Phaenocoma D. Don 1
Plecostachys Hilliard & Burtt,
  2 **(1)**
Polyarrhena Cass., 1
Printzia Cass., 2 **(2)**
Pseudognaphalium Kirp., 2 **(1)**
Pteronia L., 3 **(1)**
Relhania L'Herit. emend.
  Bremer 1
Senecio L. 47 **(17)**
Stoebe L., 10 **(5)**
Syncarpha DC., 7 **(3)**
Tarchonanthus L., 1
Troglophyton Hilliard & Burtt,
  2 **(1)**
Ursinia Gaertn., 8 **(3)**

BORAGINACEAE
Lobostemon Lehm., 7 **(3)**

BRASSICACEAE
  (=CRUCIFERAE)
Brachycarpaea DC., 1
Heliophila L., 21 **(5)**
Raphanus L., 2 **(1)**

BRUNIACEAE
Audouinia Brongn., 1
Berzelia Brongn., 3 **(1)**
Brunia Lam., 1
Staavia Dahl, 4 **(3)**

CAMPANULACEAE
Lightfootia L' Hèrit., 8 **(4)**
Microcodon A. DC., 3 **(1)**
Prismatocarpus L'Hèrit. 3 **(2)**
Roella L., 11 **(7)**
Wahlenbergia Schrad. ex Roth,
  13 **(4)**

CARYOPHYLLACEAE
Spergula L., 1
Spergularia (Pers.) J. & C.
  Presl 4 **(1)**

CELASTRACEAE
Cassine L., 4 **(2)**
Celastrus (see Cassine)
Gymnosporia (see Maytenus)
Maurocenia Mill., 1
Maytenus Molina 5 **(3)**
Mystroxylon (see Cassine)
Pterocelastrus Meisn., 2 **(1)**
Putterlickia Endl., 1

CHENOPODIACEAE
Anthrocnemum (see
  Sarcocornia)
Exomis Fenzl 1
Sarcocornia A.J. Scott, 5 **(1)**

COLCHICACEAE
  (= LILIACEAE)
Androcymbium Willd., 2 **(1)**
Baeometra Salisb., 1
Onixotis Raf., 2 **(2)**
Ornithoglossum Salisb., 1
Wurmbea Thunb., 4 **(3)**

COMMELINACEAE
Commelina L., 1

CONVOLVULACEAE
Convolvulus L., 3 **(1)**
Cuscuta L., 3 **(1)**
Falckia Thunb., 1

CORNACEAE
Curtisia Ait., 1

CRASSULACEAE
Adromischus Lem., 1
Cotyledon., L., 1

Crassula L., 37 **(11)**
Rochea (see Crassula)
Tylecodon Tölken, 2 **(1)**
Vauanthes (see Crassula)

CUCURBITACEAE
Kedrostis Medikus, 1
Melothria (see Zehneria)
Zehneria Endl., 1

CUNONIACEAE
Cunonia L., 1

CUPRESSACEAE
Widdringtonia Endl., 1

CYPERACEAE
Ficinia Schrad., 36 **(1)**
Scirpus L., 11 **(1)**
Sickmannia (see Ficinia)

DIPSACACEAE
Scabiosa L., 3 **(1)**

DROSERACEAE
Drosera L., 8 **(3)**

EBENACEAE
Diospyros L., 2 **(1)**
Euclea Murray 3 **(3)**

ERICACEAE
Blaeria (see Erica)
Erica L., 113 **(47)**
Philippia (see Erica)
Syndesmanthus Klotzsch 1

ERIOSPERMACEAE
  (= LILIACEAE)
Eriospermum Jacq. ex Willd., 8
  (3)

EUPHORBIACEAE
Clutia L., 7 **(3)**
Euphorbia L., 13 **(6)**
Leidesia Müll. Arg., 1
Mercurialis L., 1

FABACEAE
  (= LEGUMINOSAE)
Amphithalea Eckl. & Zeyh., 2
  (2)
Aspalathus L., 56 **(22)**
Bolusafra Kuntze, 1
Borbonia (see Aspalathus)
Crotalaria L., 2 **(1)**
Cyclopia Vent., 4 **(2)**

Cytisus L., 1
Dipogon Liebm.1
Dolichos (see Dipogon)
Fagelia (see Bolusafra)
Hallia (see Psoralea)
Indigofera L., 18 (12)
Lebeckia Thunb., 6 (1)
Lessertia DC., 7 (1)
Liparia L., 4 (2)
Lotononis (DC.) Eckl. &
  Zeyh. 8 (4)
Otholobium C. H. Stirton, 7
  (3)
Podalyria Willd., 5 (3)
Priestleya (see Liparia or
  Xiphotheca)
Psoralea L., 13 (8)
Rafnia Thunb., 4 (2)
Rhynchosia Lour., 3 (2)
Sutherlandia R. Br., ex Ait. f.,
  2 (1)
Tephrosia Pers., 2 (1)
Vicia L., 7 (2)
Virgilia Poiret, 1
Wiborgia Thunb., 1
Xiphotheca Eckl. & Zeyh., 3
  (1)

FLACOURTIACEAE
Kiggelaria L., 1

FUMARIACEAE
Cysticapnos Mill., 2 (1)
Fumaria L., 1

GENTIANACEAE
Chironia L., 9 (3)
Orphium E. Mey., 1
Sebaea Soland. ex R. Br., 12
  (4)
Villarsia Vent., 1

GERANIACEAE
Erodium L'Hèrit., 4 (2)
Geranium L., 8 (2)
Monsonia L., 1
Pelargonium L' Hèrit., 31
  (12)

GRUBBIACEAE
Grubbia Berg., 4 (1)

HAEMODORACEAE
Dilatris Berg., 3 (2)
Wachendorfia Burm., 4 (1)

HYACINTHACEAE
  (= LILIACEAE)
Albuca L., 7 (3)
Drimia Jacq. ex Willd., 8 (3)
Lachenalia Jacq. ex Murray, 16
  (6)
Ornithogalum L., 9 (4)
Polyxena Kunth, 1
Tenicroa Raf., 2 (2)

HYDNORACEAE
Hydnora Thunb., 1

HYPOXIDACEAE
  (= AMARYLLIDACEAE)
Empodium Salisb., 1
Pauridia Harv., 1
Spiloxene Salisb., 11 (5)

ILLECEBRACEAE
Dianthus L., 1
Melandrium (see Silene)
Silene L., 7 (4)

IRIDACEAE
Anapalina (see Tritoniopsis)
Anomalesia (see Gladiolus)
Antholyza (see Babiana)
Aristea Ait., 12 (4)
Babiana Ker-Gawl., 9 (5)
Bobartia L., 4 (1)
Chasmanthe N.E. Br., 2 (1)
Engysiphon (see Geissorhiza)
Exohebia (see Tritoniopsis)
Ferraria Burm. ex Mill., 1
Galaxia Thunb., 5 (1)
Geissorhiza Ker-Gawl., 17 (3)
Gladiolus L., 27 (16)
Gynandriris Parl., 1
Hesperantha Ker-Gawl., 5 (1)
Hexaglottis Vent., 3 (1)
Homeria Vent., 7 (3)
Homoglossum (see Gladiolus)
Ixia L., 7 (5)
Lapeirousia Pourret, 3 (2)
Melasphaerula Ker-Gawl., 1
Micranthus (Pers.) Eckl., 1
Moraea Mill., 19 (11)
Romulea Maratti, 21 (4)
Sparaxis Ker-Gawl., 3 (1)
Thereianthus G.J. Lewis, 2 (1)
Tritonia (see Ixia)
Tritoniopsis L. Bol., 5 (4)
Watsonia Mill., 7 (3)
Witsenia Thunb., 1

JUNCAGINACEAE
Triglochin L., 2 (1)

LAMIACEAE (= LABIATAE)
Leonotis (Pers.) R. Br., 1
Salvia L., 4 (4)
Stachys L., 3 (2)

LAURACEAE
Cassytha L., 1
Ocotea Aubl., 1

LENTIBULARIACEAE
Utricularia L., 1

LINACEAE
Linum L., 4 (3)

LOBELIACEAE
Cyphia Berg., 10 (4)
Grammatotheca Presl, 1
Laurentia Michx. ex Adans., 3
  (1)
Lobelia L., 15 (6)
Monopsis Salisb., 4 (2)

LYTHRACEAE
Lythrum L., 2 (1)

MALVACEAE
Anisodontea Presl, 2 (1)
Hibiscus L., 3 (2)
Malvastrum (see Anisodontea)

MESEMBRYAN-
  THEMACEAE
Carpanthea N.E. Br., 1
Carpobrotus N.E. Br., 3 (1)
Conicosia N.E. Br., 1
Erepsia N.E. Br., 7 (1)
Lampranthus N.E. Br., N.E.
  Br., 24 (6)
Ruschia Schwant., 9 (2)

MONTINIACEAE
Montinia Thunb., 1

MYOPORACEAE
Myoporum Banks & Soland.
  ex G. Fost., 1

MYRICACEAE
Myrica L., 6 (2)

MYRSINACEAE
Myrsine L., 2 (1)

OLEACEAE
Chionanthus L., 1
Linociera (see Chionanthus)
Olea L., 3 (2)

OLINIACEAE
Olinia Thunb., 1

ORCHIDACEAE
Acrolophia Pfitzer, 4 (2)
Bartholina R. Br., 2 (1)
Bonatea Willd., 1
Ceratandra Eckl. & Bauer, 4
  (1)
Corycium Swartz, 7 (1)
Disa Berg., 31 (13)
Disperis Swartz, 7 (3)
Eulophia R. Br. ex Lindl., 2
  (2)
Herschelia (see
  Herschelianthe)
Herschelianthe Rauschert, 5
  (4)
Holothrix L.C. Rich ex Hook.,
  6 (3)
Liparis L.C. Rich., 1
Monadenia Lindl., 14 (3)
Ommatodium (see
  Pterygodium)
Pterygodium Swartz 8 (4)
Satyridium Swartz 1
Satyrium Swatrz 16 (4)
Schizodium Lindl., 5 (2)

OROBANCHACEAE
(= SCROPHULARI-
ACEAE)
Orobanche L., 2 (1)

OXALIDACEAE
Oxalis L., 39 (23)

PENAEACEAE
Brachysiphon A. Juss., 1
Penaea L., 1
Saltera Bullock 1
Sarcocolla (see Saltera)
Stylapterus A. Juss., 1

PLUMBAGINACEAE
Limonium Mill., 5 (1)

PODOCARPACEAE
Podocarpus L'Hèrit. ex Pers., 1

POLYGALACEAE
Mundia (see Nylandtia)

Muraltia Juss., 25 (2)
Nylandtia Dumort., 1
Polygala L., 7 (4)

POLYGONACEAE
Persicaria Mill., 3 (1)
Polygonum L., 3 (1)
Rumex L., 8 (1)

PRIMULACEAE
Anagallis L., 2 (1)
Samolus L., 2 (2)

PROTEACEAE
Brabejum L., 1
Diastella Salisb., 3 (1)
Leucadendron R. Br., 11 (5)
Leucospermum R. Br., 5 (2)
Mimetes Salisb., 3 (3)
Protea L., 12 (8)
Serruria Salisb., 11 (3)

RANUNCULACEAE
Anemone L., 1
Clematis L., 2 (1)
Knowltonia Salisb., 3 (2)
Ranunculus L., 3 (2)

RHAMNACEAE
Phylica L., 23 (6)

ROSACEAE
Cliffortia L., 35 (3)
Grielum L., 1

RUBIACEAE
Anthospermum L., 7 (1)
Canthium Lam., 2 (1)
Plectronia (see Canthium)

RUTACEAE
Adenandra Willd., 5 (2)
Agathosma Willd., 12 (3)
Coleonema Bartl. & Wendl., 1
Diosma L., 2 (2)
Macrostylis Bartl. & Wendl., 1

SANTALACEAE
Colpoon Berg., 1
Osyris (see Colpoon)
Thesium L., 28 (5)

SAPOTACEAE
Calvaria (see Sideroxylon)
Sideroxylon L., 1

SCROPHULAREACEAE
Diascia Link & Otto, 4 (1)

Halleria L., 1
Harveya Hook., 7 (4)
Hemimeris L.f., 2 (1)
Hyobanche L., 1
Limosella L., 2 (1)
Manulea L., 2 (2)
Nemesia Vent., 10 (3)
Oftia Adans., 1
Polycarena Benth., 3 (1)
Sutera Roth 4 (2)
Zaluzianskya F.W. Schmidt, 4
  (3)

SELAGINACEAE
Agathelpis Choisy, 2 (1)
Dischisma Choisy, 4 (1)
Hebenstreitia L., 6 (2)
Selago L., 9 (6)

SOLANACEAE
Lycium L., 2 (2)
Physalis L., 1
Solanum L., 12 (6)

STERCULIACEAE
Hermannia L., 20 (7)

STILBACEAE
Campylostachys Kunth 1
Stilbe Berg., 2 (1)

TECOPHILAEACEAE
Cyanella L., 1

THYMELAEACEAE
Cryptadenia Meisn., 2 (1)
Gnidia L., 18 (5)
Lachnaea L., 2 (2)
Passerina L., 6 (1)
Struthiola L., 5 (3)

TILIACEAE
Grewia L., 1

VERBENACEAE
Chascanum (see Plexipus)
Plexipus Rafin., 1

VISCACEAE
Viscum L., 2 (1)

VITACEAE
Rhoicissus Planch., 1

ZYGOPHYLLACEAE
Tribulus L., 1
Zygophyllum L., 6 (3)

Index to Common Names

Protected species are marked with an asterisk* (see schedule 4 of Ordinance 19, 1974; pp 237 – 239)

In the text, rare and possibly extinct are marked with a ●, and introduced species are marked with a ◆.

Endangered flora Schedule 3 of Ordinance 19 of 1974

APOCYNACEAE	*Pachypodium namaquanum*	Halfmens
GESNERIACEAE	*Charadrophila capensis*	Cape Gloxinia
LILIACEAE	*Aloe pillansii*	
	Aloe buhrii	
	Aloe erinacea	
PROTEACEAE	*Mimetes capitulatus*	
	Mimetes hottentoticus	
	Mimetes stokoei	
	Orothamnus zeyheri	Marsh Rose/Mountain Rose/ Vleiroos
STANGERIACEAE	*Stangeria eriopus*	Bobbejaankos
ZAMIACEAE	*Encephalartos caffer*	
	Encephalartos latifrons	Cycad/Broodboom
	Encephalartos woodii	

Protected flora Schedule 4 of Ordinance 19 of 1974

AMARYLLIDACEAE	All species	
APOCYNACEAE	All *Pachypodium* species except *P. namaquanum* (see Schedule 3)	
AQUIFOLIACEAE	*Ilex mitis*	Cape Holly/Waterhout
ARACEAE	*Zantedeschia elliotiana*	Yellow Arum Lily/Geelvarkblom
ASCLEPIADACEAE	All species	
BORAGINACEAE	*Echiostachys spicatus*	
BRUNIACEAE	All species	
(COMPOSITAE) =ASTERACEAE	*Senecio coleophyllus*	
	Cotula duckittea	
CRASSULACEAE	*Crassula columnaris*	Koesnaatjie
	Crassula falcata	Red Crassula
	Crassula perfoliata	Pointed-leaf Crassula
	Crassula pyramidalis	
	Kalanchoe thyrsiflora	
	Rochea coccinea	Red Crassula/Klipboom/ Keiserskroon
CUNONIACEAE	*Cunonia capensis*	Rooi-els
	Platylophus trifoliatus	
DIOSCOREACEAE	*Dioscorea sylvatica* (*Testudinaria sylvatica*)	Elephants Foot/Skilpad/ Olifantsvoet
	Dioscorea elephantipes (= *Testudinaria elephantipes*)	

ERICACEAE	All species	
EUPHORBIACEAE	*Euphorbia bupleurifolia*	
	Euphorbia fasciculata	
	Euphorbia globosa	
	Euphorbia horrida	
	Euphorbia meloformis	Eselkos/Pol
	Euphorbia obesa	Kaffir Hut/Kafferhut
	Euphorbia schoenlandii	
	Euphorbia symmetrica	Kaffir Hut/Kafferhut
	Euphorbia valida	
GEISSOLOMACEAE	All species	
GESNERIACEAE	All species of the genus *Streptocarpus*	Cape Primrose/Rexia/ Nodding Bells/Twin Sisters/ Wild Gloxinia
(GRAMINAE) = POACEAE	*Arundinaria tessellata*	Mountain Bamboo/Bergbamboes
	Secale africanum	Wild Rye Grass/Wilde Rog
GRUBBIACEAE	All species	
IRIDACEAE	All species	
(LEGUMINOSAE) = FABACEAE	*Erythrina acanthocarpa*	Tamboekie Thorn/ Tamboekiedoring
	Erythrina humeana	
	Liparia comantha	Klipblom
	Liparia sphaerica	Orange Nodding Head/ Mountain Dahlia/Geelkoppie
	Liparia splendens	
	Podalyria calyptrata	Wild Sweet Pea/Keurtjie
	Priestleya vestita	
	Priestleya tomentosa	Silver Pea/Silwerertjie
LILIACEAE	All species of *Aloe* except those in Schedule 3 & *Aloe ferox*	
	Gasteria beckeri	
	Gloriosa superba	Gloriosa Lily/Turk's Cap
	All species of *Haworthia*	Haworthia/Window Plant
	All species of *Kniphofia*	Red-hot Poker/Vuurpyl
	All species of *Lachenalia*	Viooltjies
	Littonia modesta	Climbing Bells/Geelklokkie
	Sandersonia aurantiaca	Christmas Bells
	All species of *Veltheimia*	Forest Lily
	Agapanthus walshii	
	Daubenya aurea	
MELIACEAE	*Nymania capensis*	Chinese Lantern/Klapperbos
MESEMBRYANTHEMACEAE	All species	
MUSACEAE	All species of *Strelitzia*	
NYMPHAEACEAE	*Nymphaea capensis*	Blue Water-lily/Blou Waterlelie/ Kaaimanblom
ORCHIDACEAE	All species	
OXALIDACEAE	*Oxalis nutans*	Watersuring

PENAEACEAE	All species	
POLYGALACEAE	*Muraltia minuta*	
POLYPODIACEAE	All species of *Adiantum*	Maidenhair Fern/Vrouehaar
	Hemitelia capensis	Tree Ferns/Boomvarings
	Polystichum adiantiforme	Seven Weeks Fern/Seweweeksvaring
PORTULACACEAE	All species of	Love-plant/Hasieskos
	Anacampseros	
PROTEACEAE	All species except those	
	specified in Schedule 3	
RANUNCULACEAE	*Anemone capensis*	Anemone/Anemoon
RESTIONACEAE	All species of	
	Chondropetalum	
	Acockii pillans	
	Elegia fenestrata	
	Restio acockii	
	Restio micans	
	Restio sabulosus	
RETZIACEAE	*Retzia capensis*	
RHAMNACEAE	*Phylica pubescens*	
RORIDULACEAE	All species	
SCROPHULARIACEAE	All species of *Diascia*	
	All species of *Harveya*	Harveya/Inkblom
	Nemesia strumosa	Nemesia/Rooileeubekkie
	All species of *Halleria*	
THYMELAEACEAE	*Lachnaea aurea*	
ZAMIACEAE	All species except those	Cycad/Kaffir Bread Tree/
	in Schedule 3	Broodboom/Sikadee

Plants are protected by Ordinance 19 of 1974 which prohibits
the picking of any plant within 90 m of the middle of the road,
or the picking of any plant without the written permission of
the landowner, or the picking of any species that are
proclaimed endangered or protected by Schedules 3 and 4
without the necessary permits.
Permits are obtainable on written application from:
The Director
Department of Nature and Environmental Conservation
Private Bag X9086
Cape Town
8000

About the Botanical Society of South Africa

Founded in 1913 at the same time as Kirstenbosch Botanic Gardens the Botanical Society aims to interest the people of South Africa and other countries in the National Botanic Gardens. We also aim to educate members of the public in the cultivation, conservation and awareness of our unique indigenous flora.

ARE YOU A MEMBER?

The Botanical Society of South Africa is one of the largest, most effective organisations working to safeguard our veld and flora. If you are not already a member we invite you to join. There is something for everyone in the Society's wide range of activities, from hikes and walks to illustrated lectures, tours and conservation activism. Members receive the colourful and informative "Veld & Flora" magazine, free seeds of your choice annually from the Kirstenbosch seedlist, as well as free admission to all the national botanic gardens in South Africa.

By joining the Society you support those members who are willing to invest their time and expertise to protect our natural heritage for this and future generations. We need your membership and support. To join, please contact the Executive Secretary, Botanical Society of South Africa, Kirstenbosch, Claremont 7735 R.S.A. or telephone Cape Town (021) 771725.

Any donations or bequests made to the Botanical Society or its Flora Conservation committee are free of donations and estate duty tax.